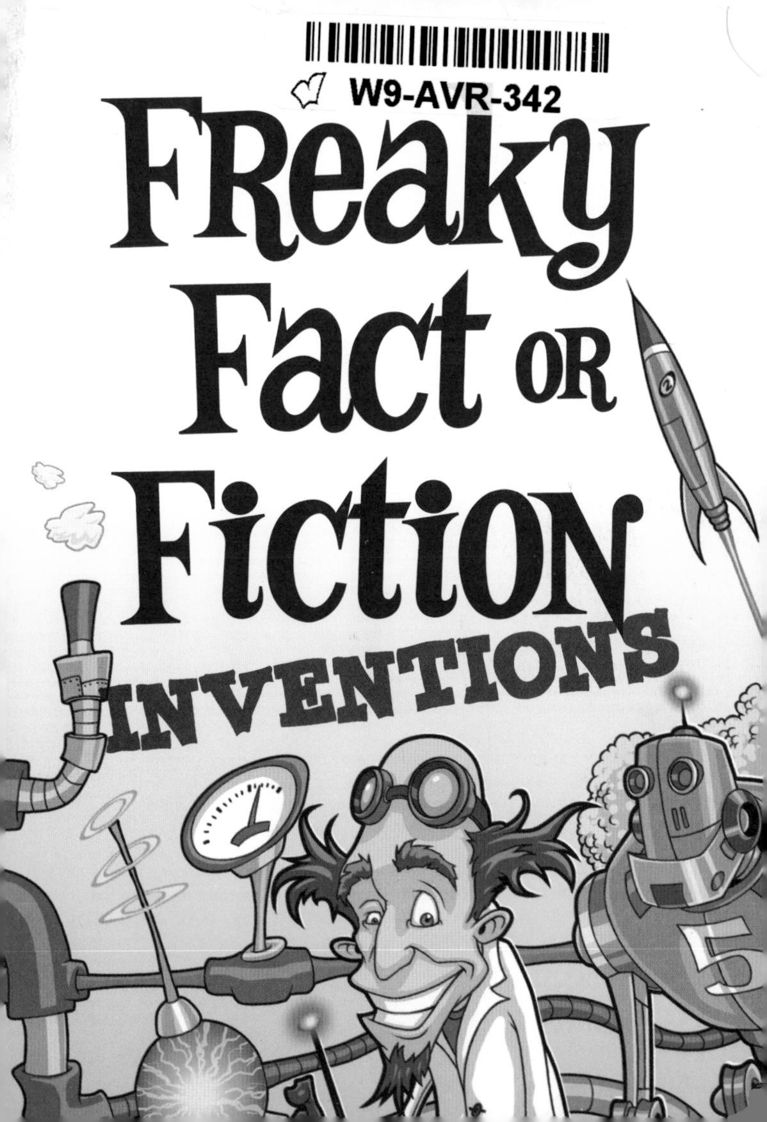
W9-AVR-342
Freaky Fact or Fiction
INVENTIONS
5

Published by Hinkler Books Pty Ltd
45–55 Fairchild Street
Heatherton Victoria 3202 Australia
www.hinkler.com.au

Author: Ben Ripley
Editor: Suzannah Pearce
Copyeditors: Helena Newton and Susie Ashworth
Design: Diana Vlad and Ruth Comey
Cover Illustration: Rob Kiely
Illustrations: Brijbasi Art Press Ltd
Typesetting: MPS Limited
Prepress: Splitting Image

ISBN: 978 1 7418 5254 7

Printed and bound in China

Freaky Fact or Fiction

They say that truth is stranger than fiction . . . but can you tell the difference?

This book contains over 200 stories about weird and wonderful inventions from around the world. Most of these are true, but some are tall tales; it will take a real expert to spot the difference.

Quiz yourself, your parents, your little sister or your best friend. You can record your answers by ticking one of the circles at the bottom of each page. Then, to check whether you were right, turn to the answers section at the end of the 'facts'.

For extra fun, we've included our sources at the very end of this book. If you want to read more about these amazing inventions, or if you just want to double-check a fact that sounds crazy, the sources are a good place to begin your research.

You can start anywhere in the book and read the facts in any order. Whatever you do, get ready for hours of *Freaky Fact or Fiction* fun!

Freaky Fact or Fiction

1

One of the most frequently used objects in the home is the toilet. Throughout history, there have been various methods of disposing of human waste products, but thankfully, over time, more hygienic ways have become readily available. The very first flushable lavatory was invented in the mid-19th century by a man named Thomas Crapper!

✓ FACT OR FICTION

2

In today's society, it is hard to imagine a home without the constant presence of the television. Designs have altered drastically over the past couple of decades and the terms Plasma Screen, High Definition and Widescreen are commonplace. However, the first (and much less complex) television was not invented until the late 1920s by a Scottish engineer named John Logie Baird.

✓ FACT  OR  FICTION

Freaky Fact or Fiction

3

In 1957, Australian lecturer and rocket-fuels chemist Dr David Warren invented the first machine that was able to record flight data and sound from within the cockpit of a plane. This machine is virtually indestructible and has proven essential when trying to discover what happened when a flight has a disastrous ending. This machine's name is the ARL Flight-Memory Unit but is more commonly known by its nickname, The Black Box!

✓ FACT  OR  FICTION

4

Bullet-proof vests are in common use across the globe for law-enforcement officers. These magnificent garments are made of Kevlar, a product which is five times stronger than steel and remarkably light considering! Kevlar was invented by a man named Stephen Kevlar, who patented it in 1966. It is also used in the making of cables, brakes, parachutes and various sporting items including skis.

FICTION

Freaky Fact or Fiction

5

It seems that in our modern age, the mobile telephone or cell phone has become essential to each and every owner. Some people even insist that they couldn't live without theirs! However, it wasn't so long ago that you had to be in a specific location to answer a call.

The first telephone was invented by Alexander Graham Bell in 1876.

FACT

OR

FICTION

Serendipity is a word that describes an instance where a pleasant discovery is made by accident. Such serendipity occurred in 1928 when Alexander Fleming noticed that some mould had killed off some bacteria in a petri dish. This led him to discover the fantastic effect penicillin could have, and the antibiotic drug has since had phenomenal success curing many basic illnesses.

✓ FACT  OR  FICTION

Freaky Fact or Fiction

7

Most people love the indulgence of chocolate and some are even addicted to it! Chocolate has been around for hundreds of years and it comes from the cocoa bean. The English word 'chocolate' is derived from the ancient Aztec word 'xocoatl', which translates to 'warm and bitter liquid'! Is your mouth watering yet?

✓ FACT  FICTION

8

Today, music can be found in many forms: on CD, on radio, downloadable from the internet and stored on portable music players. But the very first recording of sound was all down to Thomas Edison, who made a phonograph recording in 1877. The first words he recorded were 'Goodness me, I do hope this thing works!'

FACT  OR  FICTION

Freaky Fact or Fiction

9

The trombone is part of the brass family of musical instruments. The name comes from the Italian word for trumpet 'tromba' and the suffix '-one', meaning large. It was invented in 1450 but it was originally called a sackbut. 'Trombone' has a much nicer sound to it, don't you think?

✓ FACT  OR  FICTION

Anyone who has a cat that generally lives indoors will know all about the convenience of a cat litter tray. For a long time, sand was the most often-used substance in these trays. In the 1940s, a man named Edward Lowe came up with the idea of using absorbent clay instead, so it was much easier to maintain. Easier than training a cat to flush the human toilet, at least!

FICTION

Freaky Fact or Fiction

11

The first karaoke machine was invented by a Japanese man named Daisuke Inoue in the 1970s, although the social aspect of singing in public had been around for a long time before that. The word 'karaoke' comes from the Karaoke mountain ranges in Japan where an annual karaoke competition takes place every summer.

 ✓ FACT   OR  FICTION

The basic design for a zip fastener was originally in the form of a row of hooks, designed in 1893 by an engineer from Chicago, USA, named Whitcomb Judson. However, this was rather unreliable and a Swedish man named Gideon Sundback altered the design by using a series of cups that locked together. The name 'Zip' actually comes from a type of boot (the Zipper), which had this fastener on it.

✓ FACT  OR  FICTION

Freaky Fact or Fiction

13

Wilhelm Röntgen was the very first man to win the Nobel Prize for Physics in 1901. He was the man who invented X-rays when he discovered that cathode rays could pass through just about anything. His discovery was made in 1895 and just 10 years later, X-ray specs were available in stores across Germany!

✓ FACT OR FICTION

Another winner of the Nobel Prize for Physics was Guglielmo Marconi, an Italian whose experiments led to the discovery of radio waves. Not only did this pave the way for radio broadcasts but it also started the wireless telegraph system, which helped ships communicate over the seas.

✓ **FACT**   **OR**  **FICTION**

Freaky Fact or Fiction

15

Today, it is rare to walk down the street or travel on public transport without seeing somebody listening to their iPod. This device for playing MP3 music files was designed and created by Steve Jobs and Apple Inc. in 2001. They are now currently working on a new version which will incorporate 'scratch and sniff'.

OR

FICTION

Mobile phones, or cell phones, have come a long way since their birth. The first one was created by Bell labs in 1979 and had a rather large battery attached – not the sort of thing you could slip into your pocket! In 1991, the mobile phone became digital thanks to a system created by Groupe Spécial Mobile. These devices could change sound waves into a digital form for transmission by radio.

✓ FACT  OR  FICTION

Freaky Fact or Fiction

17

In 1998, satellites surrounding the earth were able to connect mobile or cell phone users across the planet – even in the most hard-to-reach places. This was especially helpful to those who didn't have mobile phone base stations nearby. The company Iridium Satellite LLC uses 66 satellites, each travelling around the world every 100 minutes!

OR

FICTION

The compact disc (CD) was created when two companies worked together. Phillips and Sony produced a disc that could store music files and could be read using a laser. It took many years of hard work and lots of trial and error, but by 1982, the first commercially released CDs were available. These were Duran Duran's *Rio* and the soundtrack to the movie *Footloose*.

✓ FACT  OR  FICTION

Freaky Fact or Fiction

19

Counterfeit-proof money was developed by the CSIRO (Commonwealth Scientific and Industrial Research Organisation) in Australia. In 1988, the first plastic-laminated $10 banknote was released in Australia after 20 years of research. A special registration watermark makes the notes much more difficult to copy. The plastic nature of the money ensures a longer life span than ordinary paper notes.

✓ FACT OR FICTION

Although a notion only dreamt of by science-fiction writers for generations, 'Virtual Reality' became real in the 1980s. The 'Data Glove', which helps the wearer interact with an imaginary world, was originally created in 1982 by a US musician named Tom Zimmerman for the purpose of turning hand movements into musical data.

OR

FICTION

Freaky Fact or Fiction

Hubert Cecil Booth was witness to a bizarre attempt to clear away dust and litter at St Pancras Station, London. The cleaners were *blowing* the mess away. Hubert realised it would be far more convenient to make a machine that sucked the dirt up and stored it, so he invented the vacuum cleaner in 1901. As the first designs were very bulky, he provided a door-to-door service with his contraption on his horse-drawn carriage.

FICTION

Just about everyone has had a teddy bear at one point in their life, but did you know that they were named after the US president Theodore 'Teddy' Roosevelt after he famously refused to kill an innocent baby bear during a hunting trip in 1902? A manufacturer designed a cuddly toy shaped like a bear and called it 'Teddy's Bear'.

✓ FACT  OR  FICTION

Freaky Fact or Fiction

When you are going on a long journey or you're having a picnic, it is often handy to have a thermos flask with you. The flask is able to keep its contents at a reasonably maintained temperature for a long period of time. It was invented by German Reinhold Burger in 1904 but only after being inspired by a similar but less useful product designed by British scientist, James Dewar.

OR

FICTION

Although the first lie-detector was created by a European psychologist named Max Wertheimer in 1904, it wasn't until 1921 that a more precise version was made by an American named John Larson. Its official name is a polygraph and it measures the amount of sweat produced when someone is lying and can detect tell-tale signs like bodily twitches and stutters.

✓ FACT OR FICTION

Freaky Fact or Fiction

25

Two brothers named Wilbur and Orville Wright became pioneers of controlled flying when they invented the very first plane – a vehicle that could carry a man through the air and be controlled by the pilot. This first flight occurred in December 1903 but only lasted for 12 seconds.

✓ FACT OR FICTION

When trying to apply logic to a problem, there are many ways to analyse the data. The Venn Diagram is one of those methods and it was invented by a British man called John Venn in 1881. The diagram consists of two or more circles which can overlap, showing how different things can share similar attributes. So, if one circle represented boys in a class of pupils, another represented children with curly hair and a third represented the ability to sing, the area where all three circles overlap would represent curly-haired boys who can sing.

Freaky Fact or Fiction

27

James Hargreaves was a spinner and weaver who lived near Lancashire in the UK. In the 1760s he invented a machine that could spin many threads at the same time, rather than one at a time, as had been the practice for a long time. The machine was called the spinning jenny. Thanks to its speed, it improved productivity in the textile industry.

✓ FACT  OR  FICTION

The spinning jenny was only the beginning! In 1769, Richard Arkwright advanced the machine to produce the water frame, which was powered by water and could produce much stronger thread. Arkwright's invention helped begin the factory-based system of production. Arkwright was knighted in 1786 for his efforts. He originally started out his career as a maker of wigs!

FICTION

Freaky Fact or Fiction

29

The sparkling wine known as champagne is an alcoholic drink popular at times of celebration. Although the invention of this beverage is often attributed to a wine-loving French monk named Dom Pérignon, some people say sparkling wine had been produced in Britain for some time before this. There are many myths and legends surrounding the history of one of the most celebrated alcoholic drinks, but maybe that is all part of the charm!

FICTION

The binary system has been around in theory for thousands of years, dating back to early Chinese philosophy. Despite its early origins, the system was only adapted for mathematical use in 1679 by a philosopher from Germany named Gottfried Leibniz. It's a system using only the numbers one and zero and is used constantly today in the form of computer language.

✓ FACT   OR  FICTION

Freaky Fact or Fiction

The umbrella is a very common object that is used for protection from rain and sun. Various designs have been around since about 1637, but the steel-ribbed structure so familiar to us all was designed in 1874 by an Englishman named Samuel Fox. We can only assume he had grown tired of those wet English summers!

✓ FACT OR FICTION

The barometer is a tool that can gauge the air pressure in the atmosphere. It was invented by an Italian friend of Galileo's named Evangelista Torricelli in 1643. The physicist placed some yeast-based liquid into a tube and noted how it rose and fell, depending on the air pressure. The name 'barometer' was given to it by a Frenchman named Edmé Mariotte in 1676.

✓ FACT  OR  FICTION

Freaky Fact or Fiction

33

The dictionary is a very important reference book. In 1623 an Englishman named Henry Cockeram compiled a book that listed the meanings of a variety of words, but only those he considered to be obscure compared to those used in everyday language. In 1755 a new and improved dictionary, written by Samuel Johnson, was published. This was updated with modern terms such as 'plastic', 'snorkel' and 'bling'.

FICTION

George Stephenson was an engineer who was born in England in 1781. On 27 September 1825, Stephenson's own steam railway locomotive made its first journey between Darlington and Stockton, covering 24 km (15 mi). George was also the inventor of the dance known as 'The Loco-motion'.

FICTION

Freaky Fact or Fiction

Although many scientists attempted to create a decent fire-producing implement for the home, it wasn't accomplished until 1827. In that year a British chemist called John Walker made a thin wooden stick tipped with chemicals which ignited when brushed against sandpaper. He named this stick a 'Friction Light' although now we simply call it a match.

✓ FACT  OR  FICTION

Braille is a very delicate system of writing. Letters, words and numbers are created on a surface through a series of raised dots. Blind people can read Braille by touching it. In 1829 it was invented by a Frenchman named Louis Braille, who had been blinded when he was a young boy in an accident at home. Louis was not going to let this ruin his life and he also became an accomplished pianist and cellist.

Freaky Fact or Fiction

Not everyone has a goat, so it's not so simple for everyone to keep their lawns tidy. Unless, of course, you have a lawnmower! In 1830, the first lawnmower was invented by Edwin Budding and it was a crude machine with a cylindrical cutting device at the front and a large roller at the back. It was a rather heavy machine, but it got the job done.

✓ FACT OR FICTION

38

Morse code was invented by Samuel Morse from the USA in 1838. Mr Morse wanted to create a system of communication that was quick and easy to use and could be sent via electricity. So he made an alphabet equivalent using dots and dashes to represent each letter. It is fairly common knowledge that the distress signal SOS is represented as Dash Dash Dash, Dot Dot Dot, Dash Dash Dash.

✓ FACT   OR  FICTION

Freaky Fact or Fiction

You may be surprised at how useful polystyrene is. It isn't simply the material you might find securing delicate equipment in a box or a foam coffee cup; it is also used in the making of CD and DVD cases. The durable product we use today was invented by American chemist Robert Dreisbach in 1937, but he got the idea from a German called Eduard Simon whose invention in 1839 was similar but problematic due to its brittle nature.

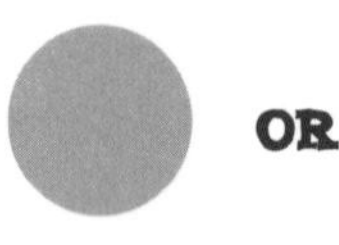
OR

FICTION

For more than 150 years, the physical delivery of mail (rather than the electronic kind) has been paid for through the use of postage stamps. The idea came from an Englishman named Rowland Hill in 1840. He wanted a system of mail delivery that could be accessed by absolutely anybody and so introduced the idea of a fixed price for posting. The very first stamp was called the Jenny Black.

OR

FICTION

Freaky Fact or Fiction

41

Linoleum is a hard-wearing floor covering used in many homes and businesses today. It is durable and easy to clean. It was invented by a British man called Frederick Walton who worked in the rubber industry. Linoleum is made from a variety of natural ingredients including linseed oil, cork powder and wood flour, which means it is surprisingly environmentally friendly.

OR

FICTION

Most people in the world are very familiar with the keyboard on their computer. The layout dates back to the invention of the typewriter in 1868, when three men – Christopher Latham Sholes, Carlos Glidden and Samuel Soulé – wanted to create a machine that could help someone write efficiently without getting writer's cramp! The 'Qwerty' keyboard is laid out in such a way because the arms attached to each letter were less likely to jam.

✓ FACT  OR  FICTION

Freaky Fact or Fiction

43

A rotary clothes line is great for drying washing in fine weather. The first one was designed and made by Lance Hills from Adelaide, Australia. He was a motor mechanic who was keen to stop using up so much space with one long washing line. He made his 'Hills Hoist' out of scrap metal before production was taken up.

✓ FACT OR FICTION

It has been estimated that there are more than 750 million motorised vehicles in the world. Back in 1885, this notion would have been mind-blowing! The first car was invented by a German called Karl Benz and it was a simple three-wheeled carriage powered by an internal combustion engine, although it looked more like a large tricycle than the cars we know today.

FICTION

Freaky Fact or Fiction

45

Bondi Beach is the home of the invention of the life-saving reel. This is a long cord that attaches to the life-saver, who can enter the water and is then able to be reeled back in with the rescued person. The prototype model was made by Lyster Ormsby but the fully-working machine was built in 1906 by GH Olding. The first successful rescue using the reel was in January 1907, when a young Charlie Kingsford Smith was saved. (He went on to become a pioneering aviator.)

OR

FICTION

Mixing gas and electricity can have surprising results. In 1910, a physicist from France named Georges Claude tried an experiment with neon gas and he discovered that it lit up when electricity was passed through it. Since then, neon signs have been lighting up streets in cities and towns across the globe.

OR

FICTION

Freaky Fact or Fiction

47

Scrabble is a board game that is loved by millions of people worldwide and is now playable online as well as in the original format. It was invented by Alfred Butts in 1931. He was an unemployed man at the time and, although initially rejected by various companies, he teamed up with James Brunot before selling the idea to Selchow & Righter. Before the game was named Scrabble, it was known as Criss-Cross and Lexico!

OR

FICTION

Bubble gum has been around since the late 1920s and was invented by a man working for a chewing gum company. He was an accountant at the time but he wanted to make a gum that was more fun to chew, so he produced bubble gum. The magic ingredient was part of the rubber plant, which makes the gum stretchy.

FACT

OR

FICTION

Freaky Fact or Fiction

Tea is one of the oldest and most loved beverages mankind has known. It is grown in a variety of countries around the world, including India and China, and there are many different blends and varieties. The tea bag, though, was only invented at the beginning of the 20th century when a New York salesman named Thomas Sullivan made individual bags to give to customers as samples. Instead of opening the bags, people just poured hot water on top!

✓ FACT OR FICTION

Thermal sterilisation of food sounds very complicated but basically it means that food in cans is safe to eat. At the end of the 18th century a Frenchman named Nicolas Appert came up with a way of storing food in sealed containers. The first canning factory opened in 1804 and tinned food was used by the British Navy in 1813. However, the first decent can-opener wasn't invented until 1858! Let's hope the food stayed fresh for that long!

✓ FACT  OR  FICTION

Freaky Fact or Fiction

51

British inventor George Cayley began designing and building gliders in 1808. In 1853 he built the first triplane glider. It carried a passenger 275 m (900 ft). However, George was not willing to act as a guinea pig, so he got his coachman to take the flight instead. Thankfully, the flight was successful.

OR

FICTION

52

The hovercraft is a fascinating vehicle that can travel on land and water – truly the first man-made amphibious vehicle! It was invented in Britain in 1955 by Christopher Cockerell, but the first working model was only 762 mm (2 ft 6 in), used a model aircraft engine and was made of balsa wood. Not quite big enough for humans to travel in!

✓ FACT  OR  FICTION

Freaky Fact or Fiction

53

The most successful revolving pistol was invented in 1835 by an American named Samuel Colt. It was used by the Texas Rangers who wanted a sturdy and reliable weapon when the war between the Mexicans and the Americans broke out in 1846. Samuel also decided to make them in a variety of colours including blue, yellow, pink and a camouflage pattern.

FICTION

In 1943 Jacques-Yves Cousteau designed the aqualung for breathing under water. There were a few misfires during the process of invention, but he teamed up with Émile Gagnan who was an expert when it came to gas appliances. Gagnan suggested using nitrous oxide instead of oxygen, and the aqualung was born.

✓ FACT  OR  FICTION

Freaky Fact or Fiction

The first knitting machine was invented by William Lee in 1589. Mr Lee was a member of the clergy and the wooden apparatus was called the 'stocking frame'. William was so proud of his machine, but sadly, Queen Elizabeth I was not so impressed because she thought it would make a lot of hand-knitters unemployed!

✓ FACT  OR FICTION

The pneumatic tyre was designed in 1887 by Scotsman John Boyd Dunlop when he wanted to make something for his son's tricycle to make it more comfortable for riding. A previous type of tyre had been invented by RW Thomson in 1846 but Dunlop used a more durable rubber and an inner tube. Dunlop's real job was as a trapeze artist in a circus before he found fame with his tyre.

FICTION

Freaky Fact or Fiction

57

Moving pictures were the desire of many keen-minded inventors. One man who tried his hardest was William Friese-Greene from Britain. In 1889 he claimed he could project images that gave the illusion of movement. The very first moving images were of four clowns having a custard pie–throwing contest in Trafalgar Square, London. However, this was not deemed a great success and in 1895 a far more successful motion picture was created by the Lumiere brothers.

FACT

OR

FICTION

Today, most people have some form of camera, even small ones inside their phones. Although basic forms of photographic equipment had been played with since 1814, the development of photographic film and celluloid was pioneered by George Eastman who founded the Kodak Company and brought out the Kodak camera in 1888. Despite his genius, George never finished school. He was a high school drop-out!

✓ FACT  OR  FICTION

Freaky Fact or Fiction

59

Holograms are incredibly cool 3D images created through the use of lasers. They were first designed by Hungarian engineer Dennis Gabor, who went on to win the 1971 Nobel Prize for physics. He worked as a professor at the Imperial College in London, which named one of their accommodation halls after him.

OR

FICTION

Steamboats were the idea of a young man named Robert Fulton from the USA. Inspired by James Watt's steam engine, Fulton was still a teenager when he began applying Watt's ideas to a paddleboat. The first test failed when the boat sank, but it didn't stop him from pursuing his dream. He went on to design Napoleon Bonaparte's Nautilus submarine!

FICTION

The boomerang was made by Australian Aborigines as a hunting tool. The returning boomerang was also made for hunting as well as play and competitions. When flung through the air at a passing flock of birds, the returning boomerang would hit the birds and fly back due to the curvature of the wood. The startled birds could then be caught by a hunting party. The name comes from the Turuwul Tribe of the Georges River area. It literally means 'curved throwing stick'.

✓ FACT OR FICTION

Stainless steel can be found in just about every household. Stainless steel is one type of alloy steel. The first successful alloy steel was designed by Robert Abbott Hadfield from Sheffield in England, and he patented it in 1883. He added carbon and manganese to iron to make it resistant to corrosion, or wearing away. Other alloy steels have carbon and other elements added to iron. Stainless steel has carbon and chromium added to iron, and may also contain other elements such as nickel. These days, most cutlery is made from stainless steel and can withstand most bumps, liquids and scratches.

OR

FICTION

Freaky Fact or Fiction

63

One of the best-recognised names associated with sewing machines is Isaac Singer. However, Singer's machine actually borrowed from the design of fellow American inventor Elias Howe, infringing on his patent, so Singer had to pay royalties for all machines sold in the USA. Although Howe was first with his design in 1846, Isaac Singer's company was more successful.

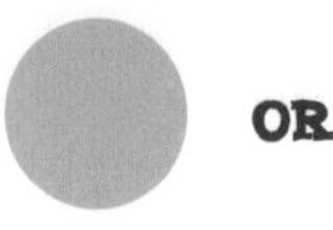

OR

FICTION

Ejector seats in planes were invented for fighter aircraft. They were designed by James Martin, whose company began a radical series of ejector seat tests in 1945. Early designs were simply a coiled spring beneath the seat but later on explosive devices were created to launch the chair away from the plane.

OR

FICTION

Freaky Fact or Fiction

65

When hot air balloons were being tested for the first time in France in 1783, animals were used as passengers. The two brothers who invented the hot air balloon, Joseph-Michel and Jacques-Étienne Montgolfier, eventually braved the journey in the basket, suspended beneath the large balloon made of paper.

OR

FICTION

The jet engine was a major accomplishment in the history of flight. The brilliant idea came from Frank Whittle in 1928, although it took many years to 'take off'. It was not until the Second World War that the British government understood how essential it was to have better flying machines, and the British Air Ministry felt encouraged to back Whittle and his designs. On 15 May 1941, the first jet plane had its maiden flight, with Whittle's jet engine fitted in a Gloster aircraft.

✓ **FACT** **OR**  **FICTION**

Freaky Fact or Fiction

67

On 8 July 1838, Ferdinand Von Zeppelin was born in Germany. His name is now famous as it was lent to the airships that he invented. Zeppelins were vast airships comprising a small carriage underneath a sturdy framed balloon filled with gases lighter than air, notably helium or hydrogen. More than 100 zeppelins were used for military purposes during the First World War. However, the Hindenburg disaster of 1937, in which a balloon ignited and crashed to earth, stopped the production of zeppelins until it recommenced in the 1990s for sightseeing flights.

✓ FACT OR FICTION

In 1939, the Nobel Prize for Physics went to Ernest Orlando Lawrence. He was the man who invented the cyclotron. His prototype was very small and made of wax, brass and wire. A cyclotron is a machine that can harness the wind in order to power washing machines and spin-dryers.

OR

FICTION

Freaky Fact or Fiction

The gas mask was invented in 1912 by Garrett Augustus Morgan, an African American from Ohio. Although the design has changed a lot between then and now, the initial safety hood was a big hit, especially when he demonstrated its use after a tunnel explosion in 1916 and he saved a number of lives. He also invented the traffic light system – more of that later!

OR

FICTION

Nylon is a synthetic fibre made by Wallace Hume Carothers in the 1930s. It is man-made but produced from various materials from nature. He created nylon while researching polymers (like silk or rubber) and their strength and durability. Nylon has been used to make stockings and parachutes, and also the bristles on toothbrushes.

✓ FACT  OR  FICTION

Freaky Fact or Fiction

When watching sport on television today, we are often amazed at the camerawork and detail we get to see. We witness the car race from within the vehicle and we can watch a tennis match as though we are on the court. This is all due to the Race-Cam, a compact and sturdy camera designed in 1979 by Geoff Healy, who was a television engineer for Australia's Channel Seven TV network.

OR

FICTION

72

Although toasting bread has been a culinary delight for hundreds and hundreds of years, the first electric toasting machine was invented in the UK in 1893 by Crompton and Co. The first pop-up toaster was built in 1919 by Charles Strite who became frustrated with the frequency of burned toast.

OR

FICTION

Freaky Fact or Fiction

Cluedo is a popular board game in which players try to decipher who is the murderer, which weapon was used and which room was the scene of the crime. This fascinating game of logic was invented by Anthony Pratt from Birmingham, England. The name Cluedo is based on the word 'clue' and the Latin word 'ludo', which means 'I play'. In some countries, the game is simply known as Clue.

FICTION

Roget's Thesaurus was a product of Dr Peter Roget's retirement. He found himself with time on his hands but he wanted to keep on working. Roget had been interested in linguistics for most of his life, so in retirement he spent a long time classifying English words and phrases. The book he produced could aid those learning English or those who wanted to get more out of the language and broaden their verbal skills. The whole job took him four years but the finished book has been around for more than 150 years!

✓ FACT  OR  FICTION

Freaky Fact or Fiction

75

If a plane makes an unscheduled landing, the passengers and crew need a way to get to safety. In 1965 Jack Grant was working as an Operations Safety Superintendent for Qantas airlines. He invented an escape slide which inflated in a matter of seconds and could also be used as a life raft if the emergency landing is in the sea. The slide rafts are now standard in all major aircraft, and even in some trains and buses.

OR

FICTION

In 1919, George Hansburg from the USA invented the pogo stick – a simply designed toy that allows the 'rider' to bounce up and down while holding onto the handles. Although there are many stories surrounding the history, it is fairly common knowledge that the name is an acronym for Pounce On, Go Orbital.

FICTION

Freaky Fact or Fiction

The escalator was not originally in the form we know it today. It was simply a sloping travelator designed by Jesse Reno. The moving stairway aspect was invented by George Wheeler and developed by Charles Seeberger who worked for the Otis Elevator Company. It was first exhibited in Paris in 1950.

FACT  OR 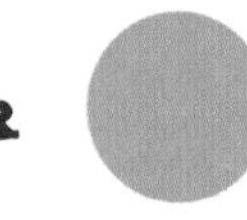 FICTION

78

Australian winemaker Thomas Angove came up with the wine cask as an alternative to bottled wine. The prototype was made by South Australian company Angoves in 1965 and consisted of a laminated plastic bag housing the wine with a vacuum inside so the wine stayed at its peak flavour. Later versions included a tap nozzle (added by the Penfolds Company), which was later perfected by The Wynns Company in 1969.

✓ FACT

Freaky Fact or Fiction

79

Two great minds collided when the Post-It note was invented. Spencer Silver created a new form of adhesive and Art Fry applied it to a bookmark! Initially, the clever little sticky notes were distributed throughout the company (3M) but three years later, in 1980, they were available throughout the USA and, eventually, the world!

✓ FACT OR FICTION

The bionic ear is an amazing invention! It helps those with little or no hearing to hear once again. It was developed by a team at Melbourne University, Australia, headed by Professor Graeme Clark. Part of the device is implanted in the skull and the other is worn over the ear to analyse and process the sounds. This technology is now exported around the globe to help hundreds of thousands of people.

✓ FACT  OR   FICTION

Freaky Fact or Fiction

Vulcanised rubber is a form of tree sap which has been weatherproofed. This needed to happen because natural rubber tended to melt in heat or turn brittle in the cold. It was Charles Goodyear from Connecticut, USA, who made it resistant to extreme temperatures by putting it through a process of steaming over a period of time and adding sulfur.

OR

FICTION

In 1904, in Melbourne, Australia, William Ramsay created a boot polish, which had rather terrific properties. It was able to polish leather, preserve it and also restore any faded colour. William developed the polish while working in a small factory with his business partner Hamilton McKellan. In 1906, it was branded Kiwi Boot Polish and today is sold worldwide. It gets its name from the main ingredient, kiwi fruit.

FACT

OR

FICTION

Freaky Fact or Fiction

83

The light bulb was developed by two bright sparks. One was Thomas Edison from the USA and the other was Joseph Swan from the UK. It was a combination of necessity, advances in science and coincidence that both men came up with the same idea. However, it was Swan who first thought of using a carbon filament within the bulb in 1878, a year before Edison.

OR

FICTION

The first feature-length film was made in Australia in 1906, and was screened in Melbourne. Most films at the time were surprisingly short, averaging about 10 minutes. However, *The Story of the Kelly Gang*, written and directed by Charles Tait, went for well over an hour.

OR

Freaky Fact or Fiction

85

Granny Smith apples are perhaps the most famous and popular apples in the world. They are edible raw but also delicious when cooked in pies or crumbles. This specific blend of apple was discovered by Maria Ann Smith in Sydney, Australia; in 1868 when she grew a new type of apple from the leftovers of some Tasmanian French crab-apples. Since then, they have become known and loved as Granny Smith's.

OR

FICTION

86

The very first rubber gloves were invented by an American surgeon named William Stewart Halsted in 1890. They were manufactured by the Goodyear Rubber Company. Gloves for household use were developed in 1925 by the Australian company, Ansell Rubber, and were made of latex. In 1964, the company developed a disposable rubber glove (much more hygienic!) specifically for use in surgery.

✓ FACT  OR  FICTION

Freaky Fact or Fiction

87

Microsurgery began in the 1960s. Many scientists and surgeons were involved in pioneering a way of performing surgery on a microscopic level. Harry Buncke started his work in his own garage, as well as a laboratory at Stanford University, USA, and in 1964 reported that he was the first person to successfully replant a rabbit ear! Microsurgery has gone on to help incredible feats such as reattaching limbs and delicate eye-surgery. Various instruments were also created by Dr David Vickers from Brisbane, Australia, who made tiny little robots that worked inside the human body.

OR

FICTION

Prior to the invention of the landmine detector, soldiers would simply be told to thrust the ground ahead of them with the tips of their bayonets. As you would expect, this caused a lot of damage when they eventually found one. So, during the Second World War, a soldier named Miller (whose full name was never recorded) created a device using a tuning coil and a wireless valve. These combined made an oscillator that could detect landmines beneath the earth. This was a very early form of landmine detector which was later replaced by a more accurate design by a Polish soldier, Lieutenant Józef Stanislaw Kozacki.

OR

FICTION

Freaky Fact or Fiction

The first cardiac pacemaker was designed as early as 1926 and was used to revive a newborn infant. The first attempted implant of a pacemaker was in October 1958 and the operation was performed by Swedish surgeon Ake Senning. The first successfully implanted pacemaker was devised by Wilson Greatbatch from New York, USA. The amazing device, when implanted inside the body, can regulate the heartbeat. The first implant was in October 1958 and the operation was performed by Swedish surgeon, Ake Senning.

OR

FICTION

90

CR39 is a special kind of plastic which was originally used in the windshields of aircraft. However, in 1960 it was adapted for spectacles by Noel Roscrow of SOLA (Southern Operations of Light Aircraft), making the lenses more scratch-proof than regular glass.

✓ FACT  OR  FICTION

Freaky Fact or Fiction

91

The Wiltshire StaySharp knife is a perfect tool for chefs and anyone who likes to spend a lot of time in their kitchen. It's a strong, useful knife that actually sharpens each time it is placed and withdrawn from its sheath due to an abrasive interior. It was created by an offshoot of Sir Frederick Wiltshire's company named 'The Wiltshire Cutlery Company'.

✓ FACT OR FICTION

Earle Dickson was inspired to invent the bandaid by his wife who frequently cut herself in the kitchen and complained that bandages would not stay on her busy hands. As an employee of Johnson & Johnson, he used his knowledge to create a bandage made up of adhesive tape, gauze and crinoline, which would stick over the flesh. It kept the wound protected without hindering the wearer from continuing their work. They have been around since 1721!

FACT

OR

FICTION

Freaky Fact or Fiction

93

Sheep shearing is a delicate and precise job and is seen as a great craft, but also as a sport in some places. It demands a firm grip, a keen eye and a steady hand, and was originally done with sharp shears. However, in 1877, Robert Savage and Frederick York Wolseley invented a mechanical shearer. In competition, it was a little slower than the speedy professionals with their blade shears, but it actually gave a much finer cut and took off more wool.

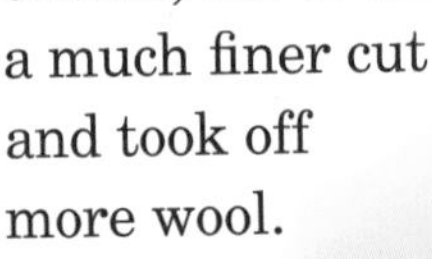

The first solar-powered car was built by Englishman Alan Freeman in 1979. The first World Solar Challenge was held in 1987 in Australia. Solar-powered cars raced between Darwin (Northern Territory) and Adelaide (South Australia). The first winner took five days and eight hours to make the 3000-km (1864-mi) journey.

✓ **FACT**   **OR**  **FICTION**

Freaky Fact or Fiction

Willis Carrier was an engineer from New York, USA, who came up with the idea of making a refrigeration unit which would actually cool down the air indoors. This involved designing a device that could extract the hot air from a room and pump cold air back in. The first air-conditioner was created in 1902 but has developed a huge amount over the past century and is now common in many buildings.

OR

FICTION

96

Meccano is a wonderfully inventive building toy which comprises many strips of metal and plenty of nuts and bolts. These metal pieces could be constructed to make an infinite amount of new toys. It was devised by Frank Hornby of Liverpool, England, and has been a successful toy since 1901. Its original name was 'Mechanics Made Easy'.

✓ FACT  OR  FICTION

Freaky Fact or Fiction

The safety razor came about because Mr Gillette of Brookline, Massachusetts, was **a**) concerned about safety and **b**) a salesman with a great idea. He created the disposable razor. It eliminated the need to sharpen a blade repeatedly for a good shave and enticed the users to buy new blades when they became blunt. His first disposable razors were made out of gold, so were very expensive.

FACT OR FICTION

Formica is a man-made material used in some floors and work surfaces. It was developed by Daniel O'Conor from Pittsburgh, Pennsylvania, in 1913. It gets its name from 'for mica', as mica was a very expensive mineral and something cheaper was needed. Although popular in the functional use of furniture, it was originally thought of for uses in vehicles.

✓ FACT  OR  FICTION

Freaky Fact or Fiction

99

Prior to the self-service supermarket, customers would go into a store and ask the attendant behind the counter for all their grocery needs. This would be time-consuming and a lot of hard work for that employee. So, in 1916, Clarence Saunders from Memphis, Tennessee, opened a self-service store and then patented the idea for the supermarket, which we have come to know so well. His own chain was called 'Shoparama' and it is still in business today.

OR

FICTION

The armoured tank is a large vehicle which is able to travel across different surfaces and pass over trenches by using its endless tracks, known as caterpillar tracks. This formidable machine is also armed with weapons. Although its invention was sometime around the First World War, various designs were being tried out in England and in Austria. However, the model close to the one we are familiar with today was created by William Tritton in 1915 and was nicknamed 'Little Willie'.

✓ FACT  OR  FICTION

Freaky Fact or Fiction

Autopilot in planes is an amazing tool which maintains the flight level and the correct direction. Although it is merely an aid for the pilot, it is an essential one. In the early part of the 20th century, there were a number of varying inventions with the same ultimate purpose but the one that was patented was made by Frederick Meredith, from England, for the Royal Aircraft Establishment.

OR

FICTION

Rapid freezing was a creation of Clarence Birdseye, whose name we are familiar with to this day. In the 1920s, he designed a refrigeration machine which could flash-freeze food by using high pressure. He got the idea from watching Inuit people in Canada placing their freshly caught fish into ice to preserve them for longer.

OR

Freaky Fact or Fiction

103

Garrett Morgan, the African-American inventor of the gas mask, also invented the traffic lights system. Beforehand, crossroads would occasionally be manned by a policeman with a 'stop/go' sign, but Garrett witnessed a nasty accident in which a young girl was injured and he was inspired to come up with a new traffic management system – a T-shaped pole with three signals to make roads safer for motorists and pedestrians. The very first lights were used in Cleveland, Ohio.

✓ FACT OR FICTION

The Anglepoise lamp was invented in the early 1930s by George Carwardine from Bath in England. He came up with the idea while pondering the use of springs and how he could design a movable arm which could be flexible but rigid at the same time. The only thing is, he didn't consider the use of a lamp on one end until years after he had perfected the arm. Since then, it has been used in homes, offices and hospitals among other places.

✓ FACT  OR  FICTION

Freaky Fact or Fiction

Cat's eyes are the reflecting lights often seen in roads in places where there is low light at night. As the name suggests, the man who invented them, Percy Shaw from Yorkshire in England, was inspired when he saw a cat's eyes light up one foggy night. He later went on to become Prime Minister of England!

OR

FICTION

Monopoly is one of the most popular board games in the world and there have been many different variations since the birth of the original version back in 1935. It was created by a man named Charles Darrow from Philadelphia, Pennsylvania, USA. His original prototype was painted onto an old tablecloth and he made all the little houses and hotels out of wood. He was the first board game creator to become a millionaire!

✓ FACT  OR  FICTION

Freaky Fact or Fiction

107

Parking meters serve a couple of purposes. Firstly, they make sure that parking in a busy town or city is easier for shoppers who normally couldn't park due to those who hogged a spot all day while at work. Secondly, they help raise money for the local council. The notion of a parking meter was thought up by Carl Magee in Oklahoma and a patent was applied for in 1935. He invented it because he was a traffic warden who was tired of having to memorise where all the cars had been during the day.

FICTION

Photocopiers are familiar objects in most offices around the world. Although they are the cause of much grief when they have their temperamental moments, they are incredibly efficient at saving time. Prior to the invention of the photocopier (by Chester Carlson from New York City in 1938), making copies of documents was much slower and was often done by hand!

OR

FICTION

Freaky Fact or Fiction

The purpose of radar was not always the one we are familiar with today. Scottish inventor Robert Watson-Watt, a superintendent working for the British Scientific Survey of Air Defence, was originally asked to discover a way that radio waves could be used as a weapon against aircraft. He told his superiors that with the scientific knowledge of the time, this would be impossible. However, he did figure that radio waves could at least detect aircraft and so the radar was born.

✓ FACT OR FICTION

For cooks and chefs everywhere, teflon created a revolution and its non-stick substance redefined cooking techniques in kitchens across the globe. Roy Plunkett from Delaware, USA, worked for NASA in 1938 and was asked to find a substance suitable for cooking meats in space. Eventually, teflon was being used in a variety of kitchen utensils including the muffin pan and the frying pan.

FICTION

Freaky Fact or Fiction

111

Barcodes are featured on just about everything we buy these days. They were invented by two students in Pennsylvania named Bernard Silver and Norman Woodland. The two men worked on an idea of having a label on a supermarket product which could detail the information at the checkout. The barcode itself is a distant relation of morse code, with different combinations forming different sets of information. However, this also meant they had to invent a decent scanner too! The very first product scanned in the commercial area was a packet of chewing gum.

✓ **FACT**

OR

FICTION

The ballpoint pen was invented by journalist Laszlo Biro and he patented his idea in 1943. Originally from Hungary, he moved to Argentina with his brother. Having noticed how fountain pens often leaked and blotted and how the ink used in printing presses seemed to be thicker, he decided to combine the two ideas to create a pen with ink that could be controlled through a roller ball at the tip. Interestingly, Laszlo had also worked as a sculptor and a hypnotist!

✓ FACT  OR  FICTION

Freaky Fact or Fiction

The instant camera was thought up by Edwin Land, who founded the Polaroid company in 1937. The company specialised in making filters to polarise light and reduce glare. These filters were very effective in sunglasses. However, when his daughter asked him why she had to wait so long for a photograph to be developed, he put his mind to making an instant camera. He patented the idea in 1948. Nowadays, the Polaroid camera has been surpassed by the digital camera, but for a long time, it was state-of-the-art technology.

OR

FICTION

The microwave oven was another case of an inventor stumbling upon a new discovery. Percy Spencer was working with the British invention the magnetron, and finding ways to improve it. While working on it, he discovered that chocolate would melt in his pocket. Further tests proved that the microwaves coming from the magnetron were able to cook things remarkably quickly. He designed a machine that used these microwaves and called it the 'Radarange' – obviously, this name did not stick.

Freaky Fact or Fiction

The slinky toy is such a simple design but has entertained people for generations. The inventor, Richard James from Pennsylvania, worked as an engineer in the US Navy. He came up with this idea for a toy when he noticed a torsion spring fall during a rough bout of weather at sea. After discussion with his wife, he eventually worked out what would be the best material to use to make a toy spring and what the right tension and length the coil should be. His wife named it 'Slinky' after their pet snake.

Tupperware is a very successful range of plastic kitchenware and containers which has been around since the late 1940s. Durable, airtight and resistant to various forces, it has been the centrepiece of picnics, food storage and even shopping parties for a long time. It was designed by a man named Earl Tupper from Massachusetts, USA, and some of the designs have even turned up in the Museum of Modern Art in New York!

Freaky Fact or Fiction

Lego is a worldwide phenomenon that has spawned many imitators. Godtfred Christiansen from Denmark was the son of a man who began a business making and selling wooden toys and other household objects. Christiansen was inspired to create a toy system of building blocks and he patented the design for the first Lego brick. Thanks to the advent of plastics and moulding machines, these bricks would become easy to produce on a mass level. The term 'Lego' comes from the Danish phrase *Leg Godt*, which means 'Play Well'.

OR

FICTION

Microchips are in so many gadgets and machines today that we tend to forget they exist, but without them, we'd be living in a very different world! Jack Kilby from Dallas, Texas, in the US, was already working as an engineer when he was asked to figure out a way to make electronic components much smaller. The first microchip from Kilby's intricate designs was manufactured in 1961. He went on to work on harnessing solar energy.

✓ FACT  OR  FICTION

Freaky Fact or Fiction

119

Original car seatbelts simply went over the lap and around the waist. This was not completely effective as the upper body was not restrained during a sudden impact. Nils Bohlin was working for the Volvo Company in Sweden in 1958 when he came up with the design which is now standard in all vehicles. This 'three-point' design stretches across the waist and also the shoulder to a secure clip by the hip.

✓ FACT  OR  FICTION

20

The lava lamp is one of those iconic products from the 1960s and '70s. It's a light that incorporates a mixture of wax and oil. The heat from the bulb melts the wax and causes it to rise within the casing; when it begins to cool, it solidifies and sinks again. The patterns created are almost hypnotic and a variety of colours and designs were produced. The lamp was developed by Crestworth Ltd in Dorset, England, although the owner, Craven Walker, was inspired by a prototype made of junk in a pub in Hampshire 15 years earlier!

✓ FACT  OR  FICTION

Freaky Fact or Fiction

121

The waterbed was designed by Charles Hall from California in 1969. It is basically a mattress made of vinyl and filled with water (which could also be heated from beneath). Presumably, it was designed to provide a decent night's sleep. Earlier designs in the later half of the 19th century were unsuccessful because a material strong enough to hold the water had yet to be discovered. Some found that water moved a little too much and created too many 'waves', so the latest designs use a form of custard instead.

iPods may be the rage now, but for many people in the 1980s, the personal stereo was the most entertaining accessory anyone could want. The first design came from Italy and was invented by Andreas Pavel in 1977. However, it wasn't this initial design that took off. The Walkman was designed a couple of years later by Sony and the greatest advantage was its ability to run on very little battery power. The head of Sony, Akio Morita, did not come up with the name though. He wanted a name like the 'Sound About', but it was his staff who came up with 'Walkman'.

OR

FICTION

Freaky Fact or Fiction

123

Spray-on skin was invented by Australian-based Dr Fiona Wood as an aid to help heal burnt skin. Skin cell regeneration was developed in the USA, but it was Dr Wood who pioneered a much speedier process which was used to great effect on victims of the Bali bombings in 2002. Dr Wood was awarded the Australian of the Year award in 2005.

✓ FACT  OR  FICTION

Football boot studs are one of those essential inventions that tend to be overlooked. For football players, they need their footwear to be able to give them support and a good grip in the turf. The big question is: who invented them? Well, that's open for debate because both Puma and Adidas claim the invention was their own. What makes the matter even more interesting is that the founders of each company are brothers – Rudolf and Adolf Dassler.

FICTION

Freaky Fact or Fiction

125

The 1980s are often remembered for the simple yet infuriating puzzle called the Rubik's Cube. This diabolically frustrating yet addictive game was devised by an interior designer from Hungary. It is basically a cube made up of smaller cubes, with each side representing a different colour. The cubes can be rotated around the axis in a variety of ways and can become confused awfully easily. The name comes from the acronym for the Hungarian words 'Rejtvény Ugyanakkor Bûvészet Idegroham Kocka', which translate to 'Puzzle Now Magic Brainstorm Cube'.

OR

FICTION

The cotton gin is a machine that extracts the seeds from the cotton plant in order to get the fibre in a usable form. Basically, the machine uses a rotating cylinder to pass the cotton through a comb which catches all the seeds. It was invented in 1793 by an American engineer named Eli Whitney. His invention brought him great wealth and he was able to retire on the money he made at the age of 35.

✓ FACT  

 FICTION

Freaky Fact or Fiction

127

During the Second World War, the people of Britain were issued with their very own bunkers which they could build in their gardens and hide in during an air raid. These shelters were delivered in a pack and the families would erect them in a dug-out pit away from the home. They were made out of corrugated steel and they were named after the inventor, Andrew Anderson.

OR

FICTION

When heading under the ocean, you don't always have to be equipped with a diving suit and oxygen tanks. Thanks to British scientist Edmond Halley (1656–1742), you can go beneath the water in a diving bell. Mr Halley made sure the submersible chamber could keep someone under water for at least an hour and a half. By sending weighted barrels of air down to the bell, a person could maintain a breathable atmosphere. Inventor Edmond Halley was also the astronomer who discovered Halley's Comet.

OR

FICTION

Freaky Fact or Fiction

129

Since the days of early man, humans have sought to make music from various inventions. The piano is a musical instrument that has been changed and revolutionised over the years. Its history is long and varied, though the instrument that most closely resembles the modern piano was created around 1709 by Bartolomeo Cristofori. This machine was a harpsichord that played the notes softer or louder, depending on the pressure applied to the keys.

OR

FICTION

130

Condensed milk was an idea thought up by American inventor Gail Borden midway through the 19th century. Borden was aware that children could become ill from drinking infected milk. Through a process that sterilised the milk by boiling it under a vacuum, he was able to make it safe to consume. The reason it is called condensed milk is because of the reduced water percentage, which makes it thicker. Borden assumed that this was what made the milk safer, but it was actually safer because the sugar stopped bacteria from forming in the milk.

OR

FICTION

Freaky Fact or Fiction

The elevator is a common device in most tall buildings and eliminates the use of stairs. It was first invented by American Elisha Otis in 1852. Although various forms had been designed previously, Otis' safety elevator promised to prevent accidents from happening. Sales were phenomenally high within the first year and soon Otis had a successful business.

✓ FACT  OR  FICTION

We have used clocks to monitor the time for centuries, but the first watch was a little larger than the ones we are familiar with today. It was a device roughly the size of a hamburger and had complicated clockwork mechanisms within. It was invented in the very early 16th century by Peter Henlein, who was a locksmith in Germany. Unlike later designs, his portable watch had no minute hand!

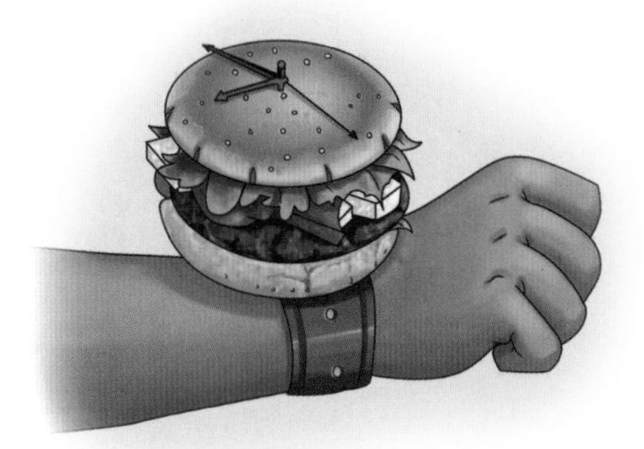

✓ FACT   OR  FICTION

Freaky Fact or Fiction

133

Rabies is a nasty infection which can cause inflammation in the brain and can be found in various animals. It is often transmitted through an animal bite and needs to be treated quickly. Luckily, a vaccine was invented by French microbiologist Louis Pasteur in 1885. He proved his vaccine worked when saving a young boy's life after he had been bitten by a rabid dog.

✓ FACT  OR  FICTION

Insulin is something that the body produces. If your own body cannot create enough of it, you can become diabetic. Thankfully, in 1921, Charles Best and Frederick Banting from Canada discovered you could make insulin from the sap of the silver birch tree. Ever since, this plant-born insulin has helped sufferers of diabetes get through their lives relatively stress-free.

✓ FACT  OR  FICTION

Freaky Fact or Fiction

The theremin is an electronic musical instrument invented in 1919 by a Russian named Leon Theremin. The machine has two antennas and produces a variety of weird and spooky noises similar to a wail or a dog's howl. It was often used to supply a creepy soundtrack to science-fiction films in the early 20th century. The weirdest thing about this instrument is that to play it, you don't actually have to touch it. You just wave your hands between the antennas!

✓ FACT  OR  FICTION

Many homes have some sort of video game console for people to play on, both adults and children. However, the very first video game was a little larger than what we are used to. The first game was designed by American physicist Willy Higinbotham in 1958 and it was a very simple tennis game in which the player had to control a 'ball' going back and forth over a 'net'. This invention made Willy a millionaire.

OR

FICTION

Freaky Fact or Fiction

Genetic fingerprinting is a term used to describe how an individual can be identified simply from the DNA they leave behind them, in things such as hair fibres, blood or dead skin. Just like our fingerprints, everybody's DNA is completely different. This notion, which advanced police forensic procedures a huge step, was discovered by an Englishman named Alec Jeffreys. The first crime solved using genetic fingerprinting was for a burglary in January 1999.

FICTION

In many cars you may have seen a device that locks into the steering wheel. This is an Anti-Theft Device, invented by Mosheh Tamir from Israel in 1985. Although there are many different deterrents to stop thieves from stealing cars such as alarms and electronic locks, the 'wheel-clamp' device is a very solid and visible one.

✓ FACT  OR  FICTION

Freaky Fact or Fiction

The snowboard is a relatively new invention. Despite the fact that a variety of basic snowboards had been invented and trialled throughout the 1960s, it was Robert Weber of Maryland, USA, who first patented a design. The snowboard is actually more closely linked to the surfboard and skateboard than skis as it applies the same techniques to control it.

✓ FACT  OR  FICTION

MRI stands for Magnetic Resonance Imaging. It is a machine that can search human body cells and discover any tissue that may be cancerous. It was invented by Raymond Damadian from New York in the early 1970s and has been a boon to the medical industry, preventing an incalculable number of early deaths. Over the years, the system has been improved and is now invaluable for many doctors and patients.

OR

FICTION

Freaky Fact or Fiction

141

The pressure inside a bottle of fizzy drink is quite large – just shake one up and open it to see the proof (but not indoors or there will be quite a mess to clean up!). The plastic of a bottle has to be a certain strength in order to contain the pressure. A man named Nathaniel Wyeth determined that a plastic could be strengthened during its manufacture by stretching the fibres as it was being moulded. So, since Wyeth's discovery in 1973, we have had stronger plastic bottles to contain the fizz!

OR

FICTION

You may have seen films in which the characters have to go through an old mine and have a wild ride in one of the railroad carts as it speeds through the tunnels. Well, although this looks like a huge amount of fun, it was also immensely practical. These railways were first used in the mines in the middle of the 16th century, making the work much easier. Before this rail system, miners had helium-filled balloons to carry the minerals to the surface.

✓ FACT  OR  FICTION

Freaky Fact or Fiction

Many workmen have spirit levels in their toolkits. It's a very important device as it is able, through a simple method of aligning a bubble in a fixed tube of liquid, to determine whether an object is positioned perfectly level. Due to the nature of gravity, an air bubble will always find the highest place in a liquid. Although it is unsure exactly who invented the spirit level, it is believed to have first been used in 1661.

OR

FICTION

Just about everybody has one or more socks. Lovely woolly knitted socks are just perfect for keeping your toes warm in the colder winter months. However, you may be surprised to discover that the knitted sock is much older than you may have realised. It has been discovered that Egyptians were often buried in their tombs while sporting their homemade socks. This is as far back as 450 BC!

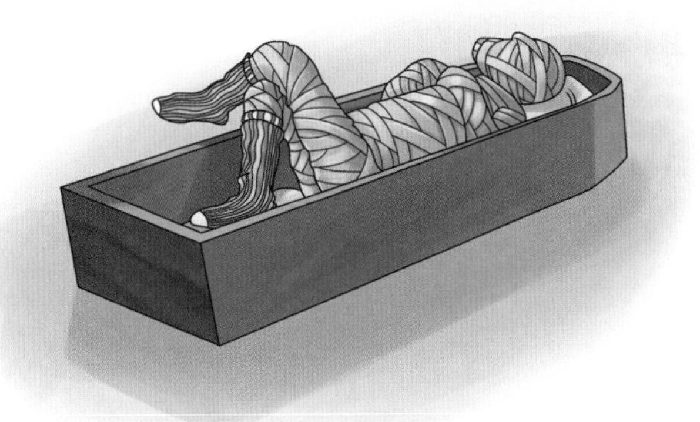

FICTION

Freaky Fact or Fiction

You will probably have heard of the expression 'The Best Thing Since Sliced Bread'. Well, it does make you wonder what people said *before* Otto Rohwedder of Iowa, USA, invented the bread-slicing machine! He patented his idea in 1928, even though he'd been working on the machine since 1912. His machine not only sliced the bread but also wrapped it in plastic.

Road surfaces come in a variety of forms but they are similar. There is asphalt, bitumen and tarmac. All are used in similar ways. Tarmac was invented in 1902 by Edgar Hooley from Nottingham, England. His invention originated from curiosity when he noticed that a road in the county of Derbyshire was unlike the other dusty tracks. When he asked why, he found a barrel of tar had spilled and solidified. It had been mixed with dirt to help it dry.

FICTION

Freaky Fact or Fiction

Although the notion of an invisibility cloak seems to be only for the realm of young wizards and various science-fiction TV shows and novels, the concept may not be that far away. A professor from the University of St Andrews in the UK is working on a sort of 'cloaking device' and researchers in California have been working on a material that can 'bend' light around 3D objects.

OR

FICTION

Not all couples are able to conceive a child naturally. Sometimes, science has to step in. In 1978 the very first test-tube baby was born. Scientists had managed to fertilise the mother's egg outside the womb before replacing it. The baby was born healthy on 25 July 1978 and her name is Louise Joy Brown. Since then, many families have been made very happy thanks to the wonders of modern science.

✓ FACT   OR  FICTION

Freaky Fact or Fiction

Known as Q-tips in the USA and cotton buds elsewhere in the English-speaking world, these tiny little tools for cleaning out the ears or for aiding the cleaning of babies have been around since 1925. They were designed by Leo Gerstenzang from Poland. Although the sticks were originally made from wood, they were changed to the paper variety as seen in British lollipop sticks. The American name comes from 'Quick Tips'.

✓ FACT  OR  FICTION

Cloning is the scientific process of duplicating a living creature to make it genetically identical to its mother. Back in 1995, Keith Campbell and Ian Wilmut, working for the Roslin Institute in Scotland, began work on cloning a sheep. The now famous 'Dolly' was born in July 1996 and was exactly like her mother. Although there may be some arguments against genetic cloning, one of the arguments for it is to help prevent endangered species like the gaur (an ox from Asia) dying out completely.

OR

FICTION

Freaky Fact or Fiction

151

Space stations are more than just a dream of science-fiction writers. In 1973, NASA launched their Skylab space station. Its primary use was as an observation centre so information could be collected about the sun and comets. It was also used to experiment with the possibilities of manufacturing while in space. This amazing piece of technology remained in the heavens until 1979, but it certainly wasn't the last!

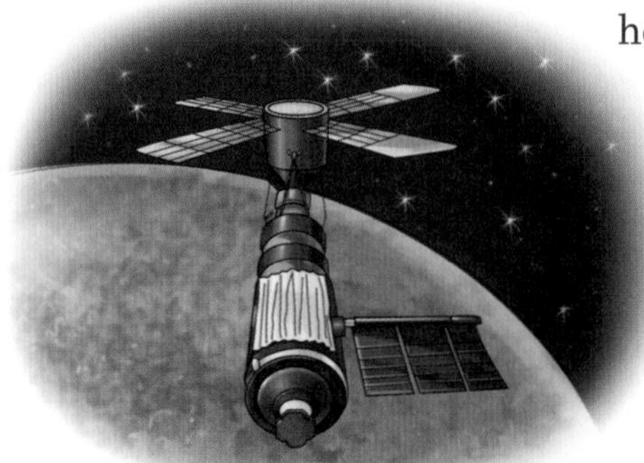

✓ FACT OR FICTION

Any fans of *Wonder Woman* will know about her invisible plane. How close is it to reality? Well, that's a good question. Stealth aircraft can be nearly invisible when it comes to radar. Radar can detect objects using radio waves, but if the object is shaped in a way that deflects the radio waves at a different angle, the information will not be returned to the source and so can remain undetected. In 1983, the US Lockheed F-117 was not only shaped oddly, but it was also painted with radar-absorbing paint.

✓ **FACT**  **OR**  **FICTION**

Freaky Fact or Fiction

153

If you know of anyone who likes a bit of DIY (Do It Yourself), you may also know that they have a faithful workbench in their shed or garage. This workbench may be a Black & Decker Workmate and it is useful on many different levels as it has various attachments including a vice. It was invented by Ron Hickman in 1968. Although it was later bought and mass-produced by Black & Decker, he originally called it the Multibench.

✓ FACT  OR  FICTION

One of life's little pleasures can be soaking in a lovely deep bath and relaxing. For an extra indulgence, it's nice to have a whirlpool bath in which little jets pump air into the water and make it bubble. This luxurious design came from the mind of Roy Jacuzzi back in 1968. During the '80s it became a highly sought luxury item for many homes around the world. Since then, the Jacuzzi company has gone on to produce a variety of bathroom appliances.

FICTION

Freaky Fact or Fiction

155

The smoke alarm is a valuable installation in most homes. It was invented in 1967 by a company in the USA named BRK Electronics. The device usually fits onto the ceiling and it produces a loud beeping sound when it detects any form of smoke. This alerts the occupants of the building that there may be a fire and they can act accordingly.

OR

FICTION

The ring pull on a can of drink was not always a standard feature. For a long time, people had to have a special can opener to be able to access the liquid inside. Ermal Fraze from Ohio, USA, began designing various new techniques to open a can in the early 1960s – some early attempts proved to be too dangerous with sharp metal bits exposed. He eventually came up with a tab that could be pulled back and tucked under to prevent any accidents. The more familiar ring pull we know today was designed by Daniel Cudzik in 1975.

FICTION

Freaky Fact or Fiction

157

The computer mouse was invented in 1964 by Doug Engelbart to co-operate with a Graphic User Interface known as 'Windows'. He called it a mouse because the cable running between it and the computer resembled a tail. Although a substantial design, it actually took nearly 20 years before it became a standard accessory to the computer. The prototype mouse was made from some modelling clay, a marble and a few watch springs.

✓ **FACT**

OR

FICTION

The fashion industry is always looking for new and radical looks to sell to the public. In the 1960s, the miniskirt became hugely popular. Skirts had never been so short before! Originally seen in Paris in 1964 thanks to designer Andrè Courrèges, it was the designer Mary Quant in London who raised the hem even higher and started a mad fashion craze.

FICTION

Freaky Fact or Fiction

159

Many years ago, when we wanted to phone somebody, we had to literally dial their number, which involved dragging each number in a circular motion around the dial. This was time-consuming for those longer numbers and also frustrating if you mistakenly dialled the wrong number. Push-button phones came about in 1963 thanks to AT&T – much easier on the wrist!

OR

FICTION

The disposable nappy, or diaper, was invented by American chemical engineer Victor Mills. For a long time, parents had been using cloth nappies, which had to be rewashed each time. As you can imagine, this was not a pleasant task! Vic Mills was inspired after growing tired of seeing his granddaughter's dirty nappies, so he invented a type that was cheap yet disposable. His work began in the 1950s, but the product known as Pampers became available in the early '60s.

FICTION

Freaky Fact or Fiction

161

These days, monorails are more often seen as a leisurely ride around theme parks, but they were initially proposed as a formal mode of transport. Like trains, their carriages run on rails, but as the name suggests, they run on one rail rather than two. The earliest form of monorail was in 1880. The monorail was first invented by Lyle Lanley and the first one was built in North Haverbrook in the USA.

OR

FICTION

Super glue is exactly as the name suggests. It's a glue that holds things super fast! The technical name for it is cyanoacrylates and it was discovered in 1942. However, it took a few years until anyone appreciated its usefulness. Two researchers in the USA named Harry Coover and Fred Joyner realised its potential and began marketing the product as Super Glue in 1958. It was briefly called Super Joyner in honour of one of the researchers.

Freaky Fact or Fiction

163

How many times have you spent a few enjoyable minutes popping the bubbles in a sheet of plastic wrapping? This strangely satisfying task is not the main purpose of bubble wrap! It was invented by Alfred Fielding and Marc Chavannes, two engineers working in the US who began marketing the product in 1960. The funny thing is, they had not originally intended it as a packing product – they were trying to design textured wallpaper!

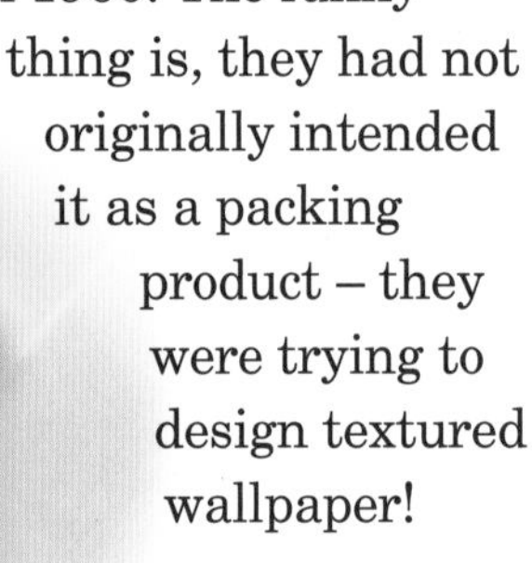

✓ FACT  OR FICTION

Paperclips are fairly standard in offices around the world, but where did they first come from? The basic design is known as a gem clip as it was made by the British company called 'Gem'. However, it was an American engineer named William Middlebrook who patented a machine that made them back in 1899. In France a paperclip is called '*un trombone*' – do you see the resemblance?

✓ FACT  OR  FICTION

Freaky Fact or Fiction

165

For a long time, sound recordings were only made on wax but this did not prove to be very durable and did not always reproduce the sounds clearly. Magnetic recordings were the next step forward, using steel wire instead of wax. Not only could this new technique record sound, it could also record data and images and led the way towards digital recording. This is all down to the Danish man, Valdemar Poulson, who began his experiments in 1898.

OR

FICTION

66

Even such a simple thing as a pencil had to have a beginning. In 1565, a German-Swiss man named Conrad Gesner realised the mineral graphite would make a suitable writing material. However, it was important that there was an implement to store the graphite and so he placed it within a wooden holder. Although he invented this simple device, he was actually a butcher in a small village near Zurich.

FICTION

Freaky Fact or Fiction

167

Toothpaste did not always come in a tube. For many years it came in little jars but, as you can imagine, it was a little awkward and messy trying to get it onto the toothbrush. In 1896 the Colgate Company, founded by William Colgate, introduced the tube and nozzle style of toothpaste tube. This was not the very first attempt as a dentist named Washington Sheffield tried something similar four years earlier, but it was not so successful. William Colgate was originally a maker of candles and soap!

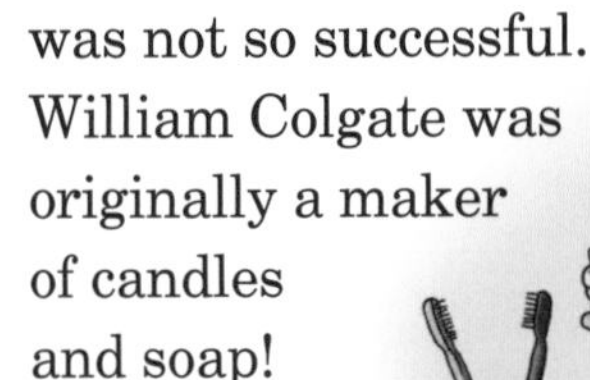

OR

FICTION

To ensure a property is secure from thieves, there are many forms of security devices and locks. One of the most famous of these is the Yale lock which was invented by an American named Linus Yale in 1861, but his original design was a variation on one his father had been working on 13 years before. However, the principle used (in which a system of pins set in a specific pattern prevents any other key to turn) is something derived from the ancient Egyptians.

✓ FACT   OR  FICTION

Freaky Fact or Fiction

169

Package holidays were an invention by Englishman Thomas Cook back in 1841. Initially, Mr Cook sought a way to help people travel from one destination to another. The first trip he organised was from Leicester to Loughborough. He charged travellers one shilling each. Over the years, the destinations became more extravagant. The first trip he organised for profit was in 1845, a trip from Leicester to Liverpool, but by 1855 he was booking trips for people travelling to Antwerp, Brussels and Paris among other places.

OR

FICTION

Although the practice of keeping pressurised liquids in bottles and cans happened much earlier, it wasn't until 1899 that two inventors named Helbling and Pertsch began using gases as a propellant in the can. In 1927 Erik Rotheim used chemicals as the main force and then, in the Second World War, two American scientists created an aerosol can specifically for insect repellant. Their names were Lyle Goodhue and WN Sullivan.

✓ FACT   OR  FICTION

Freaky Fact or Fiction

171

Barbie has been one of the most successful toys of all time. The woman who brought Barbie to the world was actually inspired by a similar doll she had bought while in Germany. This doll was called 'Bild Lilli' and Ruth Handler thought it would be perfect for her own daughter. She fashioned a similar doll and put it on the market in 1959. Ever since, Barbie has been selling madly in a variety of designs and with many different outfits. Ruth named Barbie after Klaus Barbie, a member of the German Gestapo or secret police.

FICTION

2

Air bags are life-saving cushions of air which pack tightly into a secure place in the front of a vehicle, often in the steering wheel or the dashboard. Upon impact, the bag will fill with air and stop the driver or passenger from getting any nasty bangs on the head. The prototype air bag was invented by John Hetrick from Pennsylvania, USA, in 1953. At more or less the same time, a German inventor named Walter Linderer also came up with a similar idea.

Freaky Fact or Fiction

173

The first Olympic Games were back in 776 BC and it has been recorded that cheesecake was one of the foods eaten by the athletes. (So it must be good for you, right?) Even though cheese has been eaten for at least 4000 years, it took a long time to perfect the cheesecake. Cream cheese wasn't invented until 1872 and James Kraft developed pasteurised cream cheese in 1880.

✓ FACT OR FICTION

Comic books have been a staple reading material for young and old for many years. The first known example of the modern comic book style was by a Swiss teacher named Rodolphe Töpffer (1799–1846), who would have liked to become an artist like his father, but he suffered from an eye defect so became a teacher. This did not stop him from pursuing his art, and he began telling historical stories using images and words.

✓ FACT  OR  FICTION

Freaky Fact or Fiction

175

The telescope has a long history and there are many people responsible for its invention. The facts are a little muddied in history, but what we do know is that in 1608 Hans Lippershey from the Netherlands discovered that you could make objects appear closer when looking through two separate lenses aligned together. Later, in 1609, Galileo wrote about his activities experimenting with looking at the stars with a similar device. The term 'telescope' was coined by Prince Frederick Sesi in 1611 after witnessing Galileo's work.

✓ FACT OR FICTION

The very popular board game called Trivial Pursuit was invented by two Canadians who worked for a newspaper. Scott Abbott and Chris Haney created the game around Christmas 1979 and it went on sale to the public in 1981. It soon became a global phenomenon. The game originally came about while the two men were playing a game of Murder in the Dark (quite hard with only two people) and then decided to create a trivia-based board game.

FICTION

Freaky Fact or Fiction

A fly swat is a device used for (guess...) swatting flies! Basically, it is similar in shape to a spatula but is a little more flexible. The holes in the flat surface are there because a fly can sense the air pressure change from a solid surface, so it was best to add holes to reduce that effect. It was designed by Dr Samuel Crumbine who was infuriated by the many flies pestering him in the summer of 1905 in Kansas, USA.

FICTION

178

Bette Nesmith Graham was the woman who invented liquid paper. Known by various brand names, the products are essentially the same. Bette was a secretary at a bank in Texas and with the introduction of carbon-ribboned typewriters, became frustrated that mistakes were harder to correct. So, she devised a quick-drying water-based paint which could be applied with a brush. Interestingly, Bette was also the mother of Mike Nesmith, a member of the 1960s pop group The Monkees.

✓ FACT  OR  FICTION

Freaky Fact or Fiction

179

Americans Noah McVicker and his nephew Joseph McVicker were the guys behind the invention of Play-Doh. It was Joseph who figured out that a wallpaper cleaning product made by his mother's cleaning company would make good modelling clay. In 1956, Noah and Joseph began the Rainbow Crafts Company and mass-produced the colourful clay. Although Play-Doh was initially an off-white colour, the McVickers soon supplied different colours, including red, blue, green and tartan.

OR

FICTION

Cling film or cling wrap is a plastic wrapping that is similar to PVC. It was invented by a man named Ralph Wiley while he was working for the Dow Chemical Company. Originally it was made from Saran polyvinylidene chloride (try saying that quickly!) and so he named it Saran wrap. It was used initially as a water-proof covering for planes during World War II and it was green and smelled pretty disgusting. Since then, the colour was removed (and the smell!) and it was deemed suitable for food preparation.

OR

FICTION

Freaky Fact or Fiction

181

Liposuction is a form of cosmetic surgery in which the loose fat on the body can be removed by a machine which sucks the fat out of the flesh. It was invented by Dr Giorgio Fischer, an Italian doctor who founded the International Academy of Cosmetic Surgery. The term comes from the Greek word '*Lipos*', which means 'fat'.

OR

FICTION

Barbed wire was invented by Joseph F Glidden from Illinois, USA. Although there were other forms of wire fences used by farmers across America, a lot of the designs were expensive to produce. Glidden's design was the cheapest to reproduce but he was also up against a lot of copycats who tried to steal the rights to his idea. However, after three years of legal battles, the claim was all his.

OR

FICTION

Freaky Fact or Fiction

183

Esperanto is a relatively new language that was invented by Ludwik Zamenhof in 1887. He was inspired to do so because of the problems caused by so many different languages not interacting with each other. A number of other 'universal' languages have been attempted, but this is one that seemed to catch on – at least in the 1970s when it was popular. The only problem is finding someone else who speaks it these days is rather difficult.

OR

FICTION

Early versions of the submarine date back as far as 1620 when a Dutchman named Cornelis Drebbel built a submersible boat. The boat made a few trips along the Thames in London and one of the passengers was King James I. The more modern version of the submarine was pursued by the US military and a variety of prototypes were made during the following centuries. Two early designs were called the Platypus and the Toad.

FICTION

Freaky Fact or Fiction

185

The first skyscraper built with a steel frame was in Chicago, Illinois, USA, in 1885. The architect was William Le Baron Jenney. Sadly this revolutionary building was demolished in the 1930s. The term 'skyscraper' actually comes from 13th-century Italy when buildings that were a mere 91.4 m (300 ft) tall were considered to scrape the sky.

✓ FACT  OR  FICTION

Frisbees were one of those inventions that happened due to the need for play! William Russell Frisbie had his own baking company in the 1870s in Connecticut, USA, and he baked a lot of pies. The pies were baked in shallow pie tins which had his name embossed into the underside. These pie dishes, once empty, were quite aero-dynamic and it wasn't long before people were throwing them around in a game of catch.

FICTION

Freaky Fact or Fiction

187

We use tongs in kitchens on a regular basis, especially when frying or grilling food. They can come in different shapes but they all have the same basic function – to help cooks handle hot food without getting burned. Blacksmiths also use a larger form of tongs when handling hot metal. There is evidence to suggest that tongs have been around for a few thousand years in some form or other, as seen in Egyptian wall paintings!

✓ FACT  OR  FICTION

Prozac is a drug that helps to fight depression. It was invented by Ray Fuller and a team of scientists in 1972, though it took a further 15 years to develop into the common prescription drug. It is a Selective Serotonin Reuptake Inhibitor drug, which basically means it blocks the part of the brain that causes depression. Although it does have a reasonable success rate, there are instances of a chemical upset in the brain causing varied mood swings.

✓ FACT  OR   FICTION

Freaky Fact or Fiction

189

Ruth Wakefield is the woman we have to thank for inventing the chocolate chip cookie! She was born in 1905 and eventually opened a little inn (called the Toll House Inn) with her husband. In 1930 she was making cookies and ran out of cooking chocolate, so decided to substitute some Nestlé eating chocolate. However, when they went in the oven the chocolate in the cookies didn't melt. Instead of being a disaster, these new cookies were simply delicious. The staff at Nestlé were so happy when their chocolate sales increased, they made a bronze statue of Ruth Wakefield.

OR

FICTION

Margarine was invented in 1870 by a Frenchman named Hippolyte Mège-Mouriez after the Emperor Louis Napoleon III asked for someone to come up with a suitable substitute for butter. Hippolyte's product was the most successful entry in the competition and although the recipe has changed over the years, it has always had the same name. Hippolyte named it after his wife, Marguerite.

✓ FACT 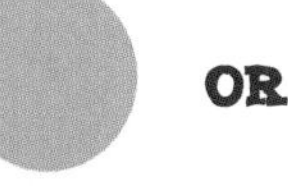 OR  FICTION

Freaky Fact or Fiction

191

Gunpowder has been around since the end of the 9th century or even earlier. It is a mixture of sulfur, charcoal and potassium nitrate. Mixed in the right quantities, it can be rather explosive. Although we tend to think of gunpowder as the substance used in guns or for explosions such as Guy Fawkes' ill-fated attempt to blow up the British Parliament, its original use was for fireworks in China.

OR

FICTION

Make-up is an important part of life for many people. It is used professionally by performers on stage or film, but more commonly as a beauty product. Although various types of lipstick have been around for hundreds of years, the lipstick tube was an idea by Maurice Levy in 1915. He realised it would be more convenient for women to carry around, be easier to apply to the face and would also protect the contents of a woman's handbag from being covered in lipstick if the cosmetic was housed in a tube.

FICTION

Freaky Fact or Fiction

193

Perspex originally came from a German company named Röhm & Haas, which was making a form of plexiglass back in the early 1930s. A later extension of this acrylic plastic was created by Rowland Hill and John Crawford from Britain. Around the same time, an American company called DuPont had a similar product called 'Lucite'.

✓ FACT

Penny Farthing was a keen young inventor who wanted to make a mode of transport that would get her around town easily. She invented a bicycle with a large front wheel and a small rear wheel which, although a little difficult to board, was easy to control. The large wheel was 1.5 m (60 in) in diameter (sometimes more!). It was eventually named after the inventor.

✓ **FACT**  **OR**  **FICTION**

Freaky Fact or Fiction

195

The SeaCat is a wave-piercing catamaran which is capable of terrific speeds through the water. It was designed and built by two men, Robert Clifford and Philip Hercus, who later were awarded the Order of Australia (the AO) in 1995. Originally, the boats were designed for trips to the Antarctic.

OR

FICTION

The electric toothbrush was invented in 1954 by a dentist named Phillipe Guy Woog. He also invented a number of other dental tools. The toothbrush was called the Broxodent and it had a movable head which would rotate thanks to a motor within the handle. Woog also invented the electric power drill, inspired by his own toothbrush.

✓ FACT OR FICTION

Freaky Fact or Fiction

197

The jukebox was invented by Louis Glass and William Arnold in 1889. Basically, this machine was a coin-operated phonograph with four 'listening tubes' for customers to use as it didn't blast out the sound through speakers. However, the term 'jukebox' did not become the favoured name until the 1930s, when it was a nickname thought up in the southern states of the USA. There is debate about the origin of the nickname, but it may come from the African word 'jook', meaning 'wicked'.

OR

FICTION

Mary Anderson was born in Alabama, USA. In 1903, she was disturbed when she noticed that streetcar drivers had to lean out of their windows when the weather was bad in order to see. So, with this in mind, Anderson invented the windshield wiper. Although they now work automatically, powered by the engine, the first wipers were moved by a lever inside the streetcar.

    FICTION

Freaky Fact or Fiction

199

The jock strap is not merely a type of underwear. It was actually specifically designed for the athlete to wear as a comfortable undergarment. It was invented by Joe Cartledge, the founder of the Guelph Elastic Hosiery Company, in 1920 and was originally called Protex. Interestingly, an inventor from Finland named Parvo Nakacheker claims that he designed the jock strap first.

OR

FICTION

Electric washing machines were invented in the early 20th century. Alva Fisher from Chicago, Illinois, was one of the first to develop an electric washing machine, filing the patent on 27 May 1909. Clothes had been washed in a variety of ways before this, and included the use of washboards, mangles and the old faithful rock by a stream! This new machine was basically a drum cylinder with holes in it spinning around in a tub of water. It would do a number of turns in one direction and then again in the opposite direction. It was powered by a foot pedal like the old sewing machines.

OR

FICTION

Freaky Fact or Fiction

201

Nail polish has two purposes. Firstly, it actually can protect the nail. Secondly, it adds a fashionable touch to the hand. The painting of nails dates back thousands of years. Chinese royalty would paint their nails, but there has also been evidence of the ancient Egyptians doing the same thing. In more modern times, we see more variety of colour in the ink and sometimes even glitter.

✓ FACT

OR

FICTION

02

Blissymbols are a collection of images representing words. The system was created in the mid-1970s by Charles Bliss who wanted to find a way of mass communication. In the mid-'80s, a 12-year-old Canadian girl named Rachel Zimmerman developed a new software program that could help non-speaking people to communicate, translating the Blissymbols into words. In 1985, Zimmerman won a silver medal for her invention at the Canada-wide World Exhibition of Achievement of Young Inventors.

✓ FACT  OR  FICTION

Freaky Fact or Fiction

203

Scotchguard is a product designed to cover fabrics and make them more resistant to spills and stains. It was invented by accident one day in a laboratory. Patsy Sherman and Sam Smith were working on developing fluorochemicals. When some accidentally fell onto an assistant's shoes, they were astonished to find that the substance was practically invisible, but was still difficult to remove as it repelled water. This led to their discovery of the fabric coating, which has been in production since the late 1950s.

OR

FICTION

04

Movies have come a long way since their origins. These days we can see full-colour spectacles with lots of special effects and sometimes even 3D. However, for a while, movies were silent, and black and white only. The first 'Talking Picture' was *The Jazz Singer* starring Al Jolson, which was made in the US in 1927. It wasn't the first to incorporate sound, but it was the first to feature dialogue. The first British movie to feature sound dialogue was Alfred Hitchcock's *The Lodger*.

FACT

OR

FICTION

Answers

1. This is, sadly, **fiction**! However, Thomas Crapper was a plumber and during the 1860s he started a business entitled 'Thomas Crapper & Co.', which provided sanitary lavatory plumbing indoors for homes.

2. Fact.

3. Fact.

4. Fiction. A DuPont chemist named Stephanie Kwolek discovered the super-strong fibre in 1965. This led to the development of Kevlar, which was patented in 1971.

5. Fact.

6. Fact.

7. Fact.

8. Fiction. Thomas Edison's recorded words were 'Mary had a little lamb'.

9. Fact.

10. Fact.

11. Fiction. Although Daisuke Inoue did invent the first karaoke machine in the 1970s, the word karaoke is actually made up from two Japanese words which mean 'empty' and 'orchestra'.

12. Fact.

13. Fiction. Wilhelm Röntgen may have invented the X-ray, but X-ray Specs are merely a comic book fantasy... so far.

14. Fact.

15. Fiction. Scratch and sniff iPods are not currently planned.

16. Fact.

17. Fact.

18. Fiction. The first two commercially released compact discs were Abba's *The Visitors* and Richard Strauss's *An Alpine Symphony*.

19. Fact.

20. Fact.

21. Fact.

22. Fact, although similar bear toys were also being produced in Germany by Margarete Steiff, whose bear designs are the ones we are more familiar with today.

23. Fact.

24. Fiction. The polygraph measures various things, includin the wearer's pulse, blood pressure breathing rate and sweatiness.

25. Fact.

26. Fact.

27. Fact.

28. Fact.

29. Fact.

30. Fact.

31. Fact.

32. Fiction. It was not a yeast-based liquid in the tube. It was mercury, the liquid chemical element.

33. Fiction. The words 'plastic', 'snorkel' and 'bling' were words invented in the 20th century.

34. Fiction. 'The Loco-motion' became popular in the 1960s thanks to a song of the same name performed by American singer Little Eva. It had a comeback in he 1980s when it was covered by ustralian Kylie Minogue.

5. Fact.

6. Fact.

7. Fact.

8. Fiction. The correct signal for OS in Morse code is Dot Dot Dot, ash Dash Dash, Dot Dot Dot.

39. Fact.

40. Fiction. The first stamp was called the Penny Black, as it cost just a penny to post a letter.

41. Fact.

42. Fact.

43. Fact.

44. Fact.

45. Fact.

46. Fact.

47. Fact.

48. Fiction. There is no rubber in bubble gum, thankfully.

49. Fact.

50. Fact.

51. Fact.

52. Fact.

53. Mostly fact, except for the pretty colours and designs!

54. Fiction. It certainly wasn't nitrous oxide. That's laughing gas!

55. Fact.

56. Fiction. Dunlop did not work in a circus. He was a vet.

Answers

57. All fact, except for the image William Friese-Greene recorded. That is fiction. The first images were of passers-by and horse-drawn carriages on Hyde Park corner, London. There was not a custard pie to be seen – sadly.

58. Fact.

59. Fact. Gabor Hall is named after the inventor of holography.

60. Fact.

61. Fact.

62. Fact.

63. Fact.

64. Fact.

65. Fiction. Oddly enough, the two brothers who invented the machine did not test it themselves.

66. Fact.

67. Fact.

68. Fiction. A cyclotron is a particle accelerator that irradiates biological matter and can make things radioactive. This is useful in the study of physics and ultimately provides therapeutic remedies for the body, among other things.

69. Fact.

70. Fact.

71. Fact.

72. Fact.

73. Fact.

74. Fact.

75. Fiction. Although the slide raft is a part of most aircraft's safety gear, they are not featured on trains or buses.

76. Fiction. The origin of the word 'pogo' is debatable, but it certainly does not stand for 'Pounce On, Go Orbital'!

77. Fiction. The escalator was exhibited in Paris, but not in 1950. It was half a century earlier, in 1900!

78. Fact.

79. Fact.

80. Fact.

81. Fact.

82. Fiction. There is no kiwi fruit in the polish.

83. Fact.

84. Fact.

85. Fact. The exact nature of the discovery is not (and may never be) known, but Maria Ann Smith was the woman who discovered them.

86. Fact.

87. Fiction. Dr David Vickers did create some microsurgery instruments, but not mini-robots.

88. Fact.

89. Fact.

90. Fiction. SOLA stands for Scientific Optical Laboratories of Australia.

91. Fact.

92. Fiction. The bandaid has been available since 1921, not 1721.

93. Fact.

94. Fiction. The first winner completed the race in 44 hours.

95. Fact.

96. Fact.

97. Fiction. The first razors were made out of brass and sheet steel.

98. Fact.

99. Fiction. Saunders' chain was called 'Piggly Wiggly'.

100. Fact. The tank was indeed nicknamed 'Little Willie'.

101. Fact.

102. Fact

103. Fact.

104. Fact.

105. Fiction. Although Percy Shaw didn't become Prime Minister of England, James Callaghan did (from 1976 to 1979). However, many years before his successful election, while working for the Ministry of Transport, Callaghan was responsible for buying millions of Shaw's cat's eyes and implementing them in roads around England.

106. Fact.

107. Fiction. The parking meter was invented by Carl Magee, but he wasn't a traffic warden. He was a newspaper editor.

108. Fact.

Answers

109. Fact.

110. Fiction. Roy Plunkett discovered this new plastic by accident while he was trying to discover a new non-toxic refrigerant gas. Nor did he work for NASA; he worked as a chemist.

111. Fact.

112. Fact.

113. Fact.

114. Fact.

115. Fiction. It's all true, except for it being named after their pet snake. Betty James thought the word 'Slinky' best suited its slithering nature.

116. Fact.

117. Fact.

118. Fact.

119. Fact.

120. Fact.

121. Fiction. There are no custard beds.

122. Fact.

123. Fact.

124. Fact.

125. Fiction. The designer was called Erno Rubik, hence the name 'Rubik's Cube'.

126. Fiction. Although Eli Whitney did invent the cotton gin, it did not bring him great wealth. As it was such a simple device, many copied it and his company went out of business.

127. Fiction. The Anderson Shelters were merely named after the man in government who issued the shelters. Sir John Anderson was Home Secretary at the time.

128. Fact.

129. Fact.

130. Fact.

131. Fiction. Strangely, sales were not high initially. Elisha Otis only sold three elevators in the first year. It wasn't until a few years later that sales started to rise.

132. Fact.

133. Fact.

134. Fiction. Dr Banting and his student, Charles Best, did indeed figure out the best source of insulin, but it was not from any tree! It was from the pancreas of certain animals, and Banting and

Best discovered how to extract it without it being destroyed by the gland's digestive juices. Today, the majority of insulin used by diabetics is a form of human insulin made using DNA technology.

135. Fact.

136. Fiction. Sadly, Mr Higinbotham did not become a millionaire as he did not patent his creation. In 1972 a man named Nolan Bushnell patented 'Pong', which was very similar to Higinbotham's game.

137. Fiction. The first crime solved was a murder back in January 1987.

138. Fact.

139. Fact.

140. Fact.

141. Fact.

142. Fiction. Before the miners had the rail system, they had to carry all the rocks and minerals by hand or in bumpy carts.

143. Fact.

144. Fact.

145. Fact.

146. Fact. The name 'tarmac' comes from the words 'Tar' and 'Macadam', the latter being a term for road construction pioneered by John McAdam from Scotland.

147. Fact. Richard Schowengerdt of California has already patented his own Cloaking System with the US Patent office, patent # US5307162.

148. Fact.

149. Fiction. The Q in 'Q-tip' stands for Quality.

150. Fact.

151. Fact.

152. Fact.

153. Fiction. Ron Hickman's invention was the Minibench, not the Multibench.

154. Fact.

155. Fact.

156. Fact.

157. Fiction. The first mouse was actually made of wood with two metal wheels.

158. Fact.

Answers

159. Fact.

160. Fact.

161. Fiction. Lyle Lanley did not invent the monorail. He was a character in the animated TV series *The Simpsons*, created by Matt Groening. German engineer Eugen Langen built the first successful monorail in 1901 and it still runs in Wuppertal, North-West Germany.

162. Fiction. It was never called Super Joyner.

163. Fact. But we can see why they opted for the packaging!

164. Fact.

165. Fact.

166. Fiction. Although Gesner did design the pencil, he was not a butcher. He was a professor in ethics, physics and natural sciences, and worked in medicine.

167. Fact.

168. Fact.

169. Fact.

170. Fact.

171. Fiction. Barbie was named after the creator's daughter, Barbara. The doll's full name is Barbara Millicent Roberts.

172. Fact.

173. Fact.

174. Fact.

175. Fact.

176. Fiction. The two inventors were inspired while playing a game of Scrabble.

177. Fact.

178. Fact.

179. Fiction. A tartan-coloured Play-Doh would not stay tartan for long!

180. Fact.

181. Fact.

182. Fact.

183. Fact.

184. Fiction. Two early designs of submarine were named the Turtle in 1775 and the Alligator in 1863 - both proved to be unsuccessful.

185. Fact.

186. Fact. Apparently, the pie-tin throwing game was popular with students at Yale University in the 1940s.

187. Fact.

188. Fact.

189. Fiction. She was given a lifetime supply of Nestlé chocolate!

190. Fiction. The name 'margarine' was inspired by the margaric acid used in the making of the spread. Margaric acid is so called because it resembles pearls and the Greek word for pearl is '*margarites*'.

191. Fact.

192. Fact.

193. Fact.

194. Fiction. The Penny Farthing was invented by James Starley and William Hillman in the late 19th century. It was named after the two coins of differing sizes then in use in Britain, the penny and the farthing, which the wheels resembled.

195. Fiction. The boats were initially designed for trips to the Great Barrier Reef off the northeastern coast of Australia.

196. Fiction. The electric power drill was invented by Wilhelm Fein in 1895.

197. Fact.

198. Fact.

199. Fact.

200. Fiction. It was powered by an electric motor.

201. Fact.

202. Fact.

203. Fact.

204. Fiction. The first British film to feature sound dialogue was not *The Lodger*. It was *Blackmail* in 1929, but it certainly was directed by Alfred Hitchcock.

Sources

1. Roger Bridgman, *1000 Inventions & Discoveries* (book), 2006; Thomas Crapper & Co Ltd, www.thomas-crapper.com, 2009

2. *Encyclopaedia Britannica*, 2005

3. Encyclopaedia Britannica Online, www.britannica.com, 2010

4. Roger Bridgman, *1000 Inventions & Discoveries* (book), 2006

5. *Encyclopaedia Britannica*, 2005

6. *Encyclopaedia Britannica*, 2005

7. *Encyclopaedia Britannica*, 2005

8. *Encyclopaedia Britannica*, 2005; Project Gutenberg, www.gutenberg.org, 2010

9. *Encyclopaedia Britannica*, 2005; Madeau Stewart, *The Music Lover's Guide to the Instruments of the Orchestra* (book), 1980

10. Encyclopaedia Britannica Online, www.britannica.com, 2010

11. 'Daisuke Inoue', *Time Asia* (magazine), August 1999

12. Roger Bridgman, *1000 Inventions & Discoveries* (book), 2006

13. *Encyclopaedia Britannica*, 2005

14. *Encyclopaedia Britannica*, 2005

15. Roger Bridgman, *1000 Inventions & Discoveries* (book), 2006

16. Roger Bridgman, *1000 Inventions & Discoveries* (book), 2006

17. Iridium Satellite Communications, www.iridium.com, 2010

18. 'How the CD was developed', BBC News, http://news.bbc.co.uk, 2007

19. Margaret McPhee, *The Dictionary of Australian Inventions and Discoveries* (book), 1993

20. Roger Bridgman, *1000 Inventions & Discoveries* (book), 2006

21. *The Biographical Dictionary of Scientists: Vol. 6; Engineers & Inventors*, 1985

22. Roger Bridgman, *1000 Inventions & Discoveries* (book), 2006

23. Roger Bridgman, *1000 Inventions & Discoveries* (book), 2006

24. Roger Bridgman, *1000 Inventions & Discoveries* (book), 2006

25. *Encyclopaedia Britannica*, 2005

26. 'How to do Venn Diagram Problems', eHow, www.ehow.com, 2010

27. *Encyclopaedia Britannica*, 2005

28. *Encyclopaedia Britannica*, 2005

29. English-Wine.com, www.english-wine.com, 2001

30. Roger Bridgman, *1000 Inventions & Discoveries* (book), 2006

31. Roger Bridgman, *1000 Inventions & Discoveries* (book), 2006

32. *Encyclopaedia Britannica*, 2005

33. Roger Bridgman, *1000 Inventions & Discoveries* (book), 2006; David Crystal, *Dr Johnson's Dictionary: An Anthology* (book), 2005

34. *Encyclopaedia Britannica*, 2005

35. Roger Bridgman, *1000 Inventions & Discoveries* (book), 2006

36. *Encyclopaedia Britannica*, 2005; C Michael Mellor, *Louis Braille: A Touch of Genius* (book), 2006

37. Roger Bridgman, *1000 Inventions & Discoveries* (book), 2006

38. *Encyclopaedia Britannica*, 2005

39. Roger Bridgman, *1000 Inventions & Discoveries* (book), 2006

40. *Encyclopaedia Britannica*, 2005

41. Roger Bridgman, *1000 Inventions & Discoveries* (book), 2006

42. *Encyclopaedia Britannica*, 2005

43. Margaret McPhee, *The Dictionary of Australian Inventions and Discoveries* (book), 1993

44. *Encyclopaedia Britannica*, 2005; 'The Holy War on SUVs', Forbes.com, www.forbes.com, 2003

45. *Margaret McPhee, The Dictionary of Australian Inventions and Discoveries* (book), 1993; Powerhouse Museum, www. powerhousemuseum.com, 2001

46. *Encyclopaedia Britannica*, 2005; Roger Bridgman, *1000 Inventions & Discoveries* (book), 2006

47. Roger Bridgman, *1000 Inventions & Discoveries* (book), 2006; Absolute Astronomy, www. absoluteastronomy.com, 2010; Encyclopaedia Britannica Online, www.britannica.com, 2010

48. Roger Bridgman, *1000 Inventions & Discoveries* (book), 2006

49. Roger Bridgman, *1000 Inventions & Discoveries* (book), 2006

50. *The Biographical Dictionary of Scientists: Vol. 6; Engineers & Inventors*, 1985

51. *The Biographical Dictionary of Scientists: Vol. 6; Engineers & Inventors*, 1985

52. *The Biographical Dictionary of Scientists: Vol. 6; Engineers & Inventors*, 1985

53. *The Biographical Dictionary of Scientists: Vol. 6; Engineers & Inventors*, 1985

54. *The Biographical Dictionary of Scientists: Vol. 6; Engineers & Inventors*, 1985

55. Roger Bridgman, *1000 Inventions & Discoveries* (book), 2006; Nottinghamshire History, www.nottshistory. org.uk, 2003

56. *The Biographical Dictionary of Scientists: Vol. 6; Engineers & Inventors*, 1985

57. *The Biographical Dictionary of Scientists: Vol. 6; Engineers & Inventors*, 1985; Screen Online, www. screenonline.org.uk, 2010

58. Kodak, www.kodak.com, 2010

59. *The Biographical Dictionary of Scientists: Vol. 6; Engineers & Inventors*, 1985

60. *The Biographical Dictionary of Scientists: Vol. 6; Engineers & Inventors*, 1985

61. Margaret McPhee, *The Dictionary of Australian Inventions and Discoveries* (book), 1993

62. *The Biographical Dictionary of Scientists: Vol. 6; Engineers & Inventors*, 1985

63. *The Biographical Dictionary of Scientists: Vol. 6; Engineers & Inventors*, 1985

64. *The Biographical Dictionary of Scientists: Vol. 6; Engineers & Inventors*, 1985

65. *The Biographical Dictionary of Scientists: Vol. 6; Engineers & Inventors*, 1985

66. *The Biographical Dictionary of Scientists: Vol. 6; Engineers & Inventors*, 1985

67. *The Biographical Dictionary of Scientists: Vol. 6; Engineers & Inventors*, 1985

68. *The World Book Encyclopaedia of Science: Vol. 8; Men and Women of Science*

69. *The World Book Encyclopaedia of Science: Vol. 8; Men and Women of Science;* Stephen Van Dulken, *Inventing the 20th Century: 100 Inventions that Shaped the World* (book), 2002

Sources

70. Stephen Van Dulken, *Inventing the 20th Century: 100 Inventions that Shaped the World* (book), 2002

71. Margaret McPhee, *The Dictionary of Australian Inventions and Discoveries* (book), 1993

72. United States Patent and Tradesmark Office, www.uspto.gov, 2009; American Heritage, www.americanheritage.com, 2005

73. Hasbro, www.hasbro.com, 2008; The Art of Murder, www.theartofmurder.com, 2010

74. Dr Peter Mark Roget, *Roget's Thesaurus* (book), 2002; Encyclopaedia Britannica Online, www.britannica.com, 2010

75. Margaret McPhee, *The Dictionary of Australian Inventions and Discoveries* (book), 1993

76. American Pogo Stick Company, www.pogostickusa.com, 2005

77. Roger Bridgman, *1000 Inventions & Discoveries* (book), 2006

78. Margaret McPhee, *The Dictionary of Australian Inventions and Discoveries* (book), 1993

79. 3M, www.3m.com, 2010

80. Margaret McPhee, *The Dictionary of Australian Inventions and Discoveries* (book), 1993; The Bionic Ear Institute, www.bionicear.org, 2010; Cochlear, www.cochlear.com, 2010

81. *The Biographical Dictionary of Scientists: Vol. 6; Engineers & Inventors*, 1985

82. Margaret McPhee, *The Dictionary of Australian Inventions and Discoveries* (book), 1993

83. Roger Bridgman, *1000 Inventions & Discoveries* (book), 2006

84. Margaret McPhee, *The Dictionary of Australian Inventions and Discoveries* (book), 1993

85. Margaret McPhee, *The Dictionary of Australian Inventions and Discoveries* (book), 1993

86. Margaret McPhee, *The Dictionary of Australian Inventions and Discoveries* (book), 1993; *Encyclopaedia Britannica*, 1983; PubMed Central, www.ncbi.nlm.nih.gov/pmc, 2006

87. Margaret McPhee, *The Dictionary of Australian Inventions and Discoveries* (book), 1993; Microsurgeon.org, www.microsurgeon.org, 2010

88. Margaret McPhee, *The Dictionary of Australian Inventions and Discoveries* (book), 1993; Mike Croll, *The History of Landmines* (book) 1998

89. Margaret McPhee, *The Dictionary of Australian Inventions and Discoveries* (book), 1993; Stephen Van Dulken, *Inventing the 20th Century: 100 Inventions that Shaped the World* (book), 2002; Heart Rhythm Society, www.hrsonline.org, 1998

90. Margaret McPhee, *The Dictionary of Australian Inventions and Discoveries* (book), 1993

91. Margaret McPhee, *The Dictionary of Australian Inventions and Discoveries* (book), 1993

92. Johnson & Johnson, www.jnj.com, 2010

93. Margaret McPhee, *The Dictionary of Australian Inventions and Discoveries* (book), 1993

94. Margaret McPhee, *The Dictionary of Australian Inventions and Discoveries* (book), 1993; Solar Powered Cars, www.solarpoweredcars.net, 2010; Global Green Challenge, www.globalgreenchallenge.com.au, 2010

95. *Encyclopaedia Britannica*, 2005

96. Stephen Van Dulken, *Inventing the 20th Century: 100 Inventions that Shaped the World* (book), 2002

97. Stephen Van Dulken, *Inventing the 20th Century: 100 Inventions that Shaped the World* (book), 2002

98. Stephen Van Dulken, *Inventing the 20th Century: 100 Inventions that Shaped the World* (book), 2002

Sources

99. Stephen Van Dulken, *Inventing the 20th Century: 100 Inventions that Shaped the World* (book), 2002

100. HP Willmott, *World War I* (book), 2003

101. Stephen Van Dulken, *Inventing the 20th Century: 100 Inventions that Shaped the World* (book), 2002

102. Stephen Van Dulken, *Inventing the 20th Century: 100 Inventions that Shaped the World* (book), 2002

103. Stephen Van Dulken, *Inventing the 20th Century: 100 Inventions that Shaped the World* (book), 2002

104. Stephen Van Dulken, *Inventing the 20th Century: 100 Inventions that Shaped the World* (book), 2002

105. Stephen Van Dulken, *Inventing the 20th Century: 100 Inventions that Shaped the World* (book), 2002

106. Stephen Van Dulken, *Inventing the 20th Century: 100 Inventions that Shaped the World* (book), 2002

107. Stephen Van Dulken, *Inventing the 20th Century: 100 Inventions that Shaped the World* (book), 2002

108. Stephen Van Dulken, *Inventing the 20th Century: 100 Inventions that Shaped the World* (book), 2002

109. Stephen Van Dulken, *Inventing the 20th Century: 100 Inventions that Shaped the World* (book), 2002

110. Stephen Van Dulken, *Inventing the 20th Century: 100 Inventions that Shaped the World* (book), 2002

111. Stephen Van Dulken, *Inventing the 20th Century: 100 Inventions that Shaped the World* (book), 2002

112. Stephen Van Dulken, *Inventing the 20th Century: 100 Inventions that Shaped the World* (book), 2002

113. Stephen Van Dulken, *Inventing the 20th Century: 100 Inventions that Shaped the World* (book), 2002

114. Stephen Van Dulken, *Inventing the 20th Century: 100 Inventions that Shaped the World* (book), 2002

115. Stephen Van Dulken, *Inventing the 20th Century: 100 Inventions that Shaped the World* (book), 2002

116. Stephen Van Dulken, *Inventing the 20th Century: 100 Inventions that Shaped the World* (book), 2002

117. Stephen Van Dulken, *Inventing the 20th Century: 100 Inventions that Shaped the World* (book), 2002

118. Stephen Van Dulken, *Inventing the 20th Century: 100 Inventions that Shaped the World* (book), 2002

119. Stephen Van Dulken, *Inventing the 20th Century: 100 Inventions that Shaped the World* (book), 2002

120. Stephen Van Dulken, *Inventing the 20th Century: 100 Inventions that Shaped the World* (book), 2002

121. Stephen Van Dulken, *Inventing the 20th Century: 100 Inventions that Shaped the World* (book), 2002

122. Stephen Van Dulken, *Inventing the 20th Century: 100 Inventions that Shaped the World* (book), 2002

123. ABC Queensland, www.abc.net.au/queensland, 2005

124. Footy-boots.com, www.footyboots.com, 2010; Talk Football, www.talkfootball.co.uk, 2009

125. Stephen Van Dulken, *Inventing the 20th Century: 100 Inventions that Shaped the World* (book), 2002

126. Roger Bridgman, *1000 Inventions & Discoveries* (book), 2006

127. *World War II Day by Day* (book), 2004

128. Roger Bridgman, *1000 Inventions & Discoveries* (book), 2006

129. 'A History of the Piano from 1709 to 1980', UK Piano, www.uk-piano.org, 2010

130. Roger Bridgman, *1000 Inventions & Discoveries* (book), 2006

131. Otis Worldwide, www.otisworldwide.com, 2010

132. Roger Bridgman, *1000 Inventions & Discoveries* (book), 2006

133. Roger Bridgman, *1000 Inventions & Discoveries* (book), 2006

134. Roger Bridgman, *1000 Inventions & Discoveries* (book), 2006

135. Theremin World, www.thereminworld.com, 2009

136. Stephen Van Dulken, *Inventing the 20th Century: 100 Inventions that Shaped the World* (book), 2002

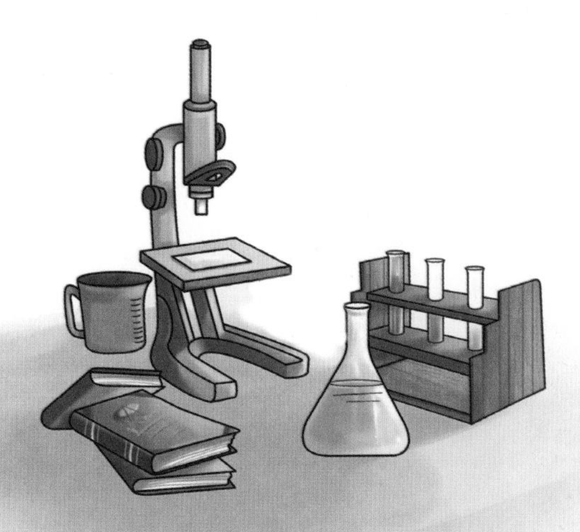

Sources

137. Stephen Van Dulken, *Inventing the 20th Century: 100 Inventions that Shaped the World* (book), 2002

138. Stephen Van Dulken, *Inventing the 20th Century: 100 Inventions that Shaped the World* (book), 2002

139. Stephen Van Dulken, *Inventing the 20th Century: 100 Inventions that Shaped the World* (book), 2002

140. Stephen Van Dulken, *Inventing the 20th Century: 100 Inventions that Shaped the World* (book), 2002

141. Roger Bridgman, *1000 Inventions & Discoveries* (book), 2006

142. Roger Bridgman, *1000 Inventions & Discoveries* (book), 2006

143. Roger Bridgman, *1000 Inventions & Discoveries* (book), 2006

144. Roger Bridgman, *1000 Inventions & Discoveries* (book), 2006

145. Stephen Van Dulken, *Inventing the 20th Century: 100 Inventions that Shaped the World* (book), 2002

146. Stephen Van Dulken, *Inventing the 20th Century: 100 Inventions that Shaped the World* (book), 2002

147. 'We Have the Technology!', *Torchwood Magazine* (magazine), UK, May/June 2010; Boliven Patents, www.boliven.com, 2010

148. Roger Bridgman, *1000 Inventions & Discoveries* (book), 2006; 'On this Day, 25 July', BBC news, http://news.bbc.co.uk, 2008

149. Roger Bridgman, *1000 Inventions & Discoveries* (book), 2006; Enchanted Learning, www.enchantedlearning.com, 2010

150. Stephen Van Dulken, *Inventing the 20th Century: 100 Inventions that Shaped the World* (book) 2002; Roger Bridgman, *1000 Inventions & Discoveries* (book), 2006

151. Roger Bridgman, *1000 Inventions & Discoveries* (book), 2006

152. Roger Bridgman, *1000 Inventions & Discoveries* (book), 2006

153. Roger Bridgman, *1000 Inventions & Discoveries* (book), 2006

154. Jacuzzi, www.jacuzzi.com, 2010; Roger Bridgman, *1000 Inventions & Discoveries* (book), 2006

155. Roger Bridgman, *1000 Inventions & Discoveries* (book), 2006

156. Ohio History Central, www.ohiohistorycentral.org, 2010; Vestal Design, www.vestaldesign.com, 2006

157. About.com, http://inventors.about.com, 2010; Roger Bridgman, *1000 Inventions & Discoveries* (book), 2006

158. Roger Bridgman, *1000 Inventions & Discoveries* (book), 2006

159. Roger Bridgman, *1000 Inventions & Discoveries* (book), 2006

160. Pampers, www.pampers.com, 2010; Roger Bridgman, *1000 Inventions & Discoveries* (book), 2006

161. Roger Bridgman, *1000 Inventions & Discoveries* (book), 2006

162. The Original Super Glue Corporation, www.supergluecorp.com, 2010

163. Roger Bridgman, *1000 Inventions & Discoveries* (book), 2006

164. Roger Bridgman, *1000 Inventions & Discoveries* (book), 2006

165. Roger Bridgman, *1000 Inventions & Discoveries* (book), 2006

166. Art Directory, www.conrad-gessner.com; Roger Bridgman, *1000 Inventions & Discoveries* (book), 2006

167. Roger Bridgman, *1000 Inventions & Discoveries* (book), 2006

168. Roger Bridgman, *1000 Inventions & Discoveries* (book), 2006

169. Thomas Cook, www.thomascook.com, 2010

170. About Aerosols, www.aboutaerosols.com, 2008

171. Barbie, www.barbiemedia.com, 2010

172. Consumer Affairs, www.consumeraffairs.com, 2006

173. Passionate About Food, www.passionateaboutfood.net, 2001

174. Lambiek, www.lambiek.net, 2009

175. 'An early history of the telescope', Antique Telescopes, www.antiquetelescopes.org; Roger Bridgman, *1000 Inventions & Discoveries* (book), 2006

176. The Great Idea Finder, www.ideafinder.com, 2005

177. 'Fly Swatter', Spiritus Temporis, www.spiritus-temporis.com, 2005

178. Famous Women Inventors, www.women-inventors.com, 2008

179. 'Play-Doh', Ohio History Central, www.ohiohistorycentral.org, 2010

180. Gourmet Britain, www.gourmetbritain.com, 2010; Roger Bridgman, *1000 Inventions & Discoveries* (book), 2006

181. European Society of Aesthetic Surgery, www.eusas.com, 2007

182. Devil's Rope Museum, www.barbwiremuseum.com, 2007; Roger Bridgman, *1000 Inventions & Discoveries* (book), 2006

183. Roger Bridgman, *1000 Inventions & Discoveries* (book), 2006

184. 'Submarine Technology through the Years', United States Navy, www.navy.mil, 2000; Dutch Submarines, www.dutchsubmarines.com, 2005

185. 'Tracing the History of the Skyscraper', Suite 101, http://architecture.suite101.com, 2008

186. 'History of Frisbees', Essortment, www.essortment.com, 2002

187. Roger Bridgman, *1000 Inventions & Discoveries* (book), 2006

188. Roger Bridgman, *1000 Inventions & Discoveries* (book), 2006

189. Women Inventors, www.women-inventors.com, 2008

190. Buttery Spreads, www.margarine.org, 2009

191. Kidipede, www.historyforkids.org, 2009; Roger Bridgman, *1000 Inventions & Discoveries* (book), 2006

192. Roger Bridgman, *1000 Inventions & Discoveries* (book), 2006

193. Alternative plastics, www.alternativeplastics.co.uk, 2006; Roger Bridgman, *1000 Inventions & Discoveries* (book), 2006

194. Peugeot, www.peugeot.mainspot.net, 2006

195. Margaret McPhee, *The Dictionary of Australian Inventions and Discoveries* (book), 1993; It's an Honour, www.itsanhonour.gov.au, 2010

196. Broxo, http://eu.broxo.com, 2009; Fein, www.fein.com, 2010

Sources

197. 'History of the Jukebox', Craig Williams Promotions, www.craigwilliams.com.au, 2007

198. Women Inventors, www.women-inventors.com, 2008

199. About.com, http://inventors.about.com, 2010; Trivia-Library.com, www.trivia-library.com, 2004

200. Stephen Van Dulken, *Inventing the 20th Century: 100 Inventions that Shaped the World* (book), 2002

201. Nail Care Salon, www.nailcaresalon.com, 2007; King Tut, www.king-tut.org.uk, 2009

202. Women Inventors, www.women-inventors.com, 2008; Blissymbolics Communication International, www.blissymbolics.org, 2010

203. Women Inventors, www.women-inventors.com, 2008

204. Colin Larkin, *The Encyclopedia of Stage & Film Musicals* (book),1999; Paul Condon and Jim Sangster, *The Complete Hitchcock* (book), 1999